Cheap AND Easy!

REFRIGERATOR REPAIR

7th EDITION

Written ESPECIALLY for Do-It-Yourselfers, Trade Schools, and other "green" technicians!

By Douglas Emley

Distributed exclusively by:

EB Marketing Group

Lake Havasu City, AZ ● 800-400-3026 ● http://www.appliancerepair.net

Special Thanks to technical consultants Dick Miller, Jose Hernandez,and Woody Randolph, whose collective decades of experience as field appliance service technicians are reflected in the technical information and procedures described in this publication.

Distributed exclusively by:
EB Marketing Group
597 N. Lake Havasu Ave.
Lake Havasu City, AZ 86403
Phone: (800) 400-3026 Fax (800) 400-4419

Printed in the United States of America

HOW TO USE THIS BOOK

STEP 1: READ THE DISCLAIMERS ON THE PREVIOUS PAGE. This book is intended for use by people who have a bit of mechanical experience or aptitude, and just need a little coaching when it comes to appliances. If you don't fit that category, don't use this book! We're all bloomin' lawyers these days, y'know? If you break something or hurt yourself, no one is responsible but **YOU**; not the author, the publisher, the guy or the store who sold you this book, or anyone else. Only **YOU** are responsible, and just by using this book, you're agreeing to that and more. If you don't understand the disclaimers, get a lawyer to translate them **before** you start working.

Read the safety and repair precautions in section 3-4. These should help you avoid making too many *really* bad mistakes.

STEP 2: READ CHAPTERS 1, 2 & 3: Know what kind of refrigerator you have and basically how it works. When you go to the appliance parts dealer, have the nameplate information at hand. Have the proper tools at hand, and know how to use them.

STEP 3: SCAN THE BLOCKS BELOW FOR YOUR SYMPTOMS. When you find them, go to the appropriate chapter or section and follow the instructions. If you don't see your symptoms in the chart below, read through Chapter 7. It might help you figure out for yourself what's wrong.

STEP 4: FIX THE BLOOMIN' THING! If you can, of course. If you're just too confused, or if the book recommends calling a technician for a complex operation, call one.

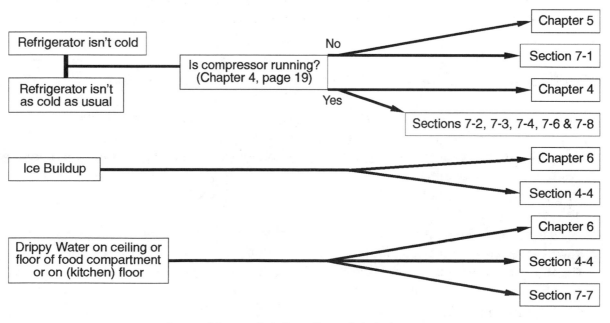

Any problems other than those listed above
read through Chapter 7

FOREWORD: WHAT THIS BOOK WILL DO FOR YOU
(and what it won't!)

This book **will** tell you how to fix your vapor-compression domestic (home) refrigerator and freezer units. (This represents 99+ percent of the home refrigerators in service today.)

This book **will not** tell you how to fix your gas refrigerator, home air conditioner, industrial or commercial or any very large air conditioning or refrigeration unit. The support and control systems for such units are usually very similar in function to those of smaller units, but vastly different in design, service and repair.

We **will** show you the easiest and/or fastest method of diagnosing and repairing your refrigerator.

We **will not necessarily** show you the cheapest way of doing something. Sometimes, when the cost of a part is just a few dollars, we advocate replacing the part rather than re-building it. We also sometimes advocate replacement of an inexpensive part, whether it's good or bad, as a simplified method of diagnosis or as a preventive measure.

We **will** use only the simplest of tools; tools that a well-equipped home mechanic is likely to have and to know how to use, including a VOM.

We **will not** advocate your buying several hundred dollars' worth of exotic equipment or getting advanced technical training to make a one-time repair. It will usually cost you less to have a professional perform this type of repair. Such repairs represent only a very small percentage of all needed repairs.

We **do not** discuss the vapor compression cycle, thermodynamic laws, specific heat, latent heat, sensible heat, measurement of heat, molecular theory, cutting, brazing, capillaries and expansion valves, compressor operation, condenser operation, evaporator operation, driers or Freons 11, 12, 13, 22, 113, 114, 500, or 502. There are already many very well-written textbooks on these subjects and most of them are not likely to be pertinent to the job at hand; fixing your fridge!

We **do** discuss rudimentary heat flow and airflow, frost, drainage, and simple electrical circuits.

You are expected to know some simple natural laws. For example; when you compress a gas, it warms up; warm air rises by convection; air usually has humidity; water can be found in a solid state (ice), a liquid state, or a gaseous state (steam or humidity).

You should know how to cut, strip, and splice wire with crimp-on connectors, wire nuts and electrical tape. You should know how to measure voltage and how to test for continuity with a VOM (Volt-Ohm Meter). If you have an ammeter, you should know how and where to measure the current in amps. If you don't know how to use these meters, there's a brief course on how to use them (for *our* purposes *only*) in section 3-3. See section 3-2 before you buy either or both of these meters.

A given procedure was only included in this book if it passed the following criteria:

1) The job is something that the average couch potato can complete in one afternoon, with no prior knowledge of the machine, with tools a normal home handyman is likely to have.

2) The parts and/or special tools required to complete the job are easily found and not too expensive.

3) The problem is a common one; occuring more frequently than just one out of a hundred machines.

Certain mildly expensive repairs may be included in this book, if they pass the following criteria:

1) The cost of the repair is still far less than replacing the machine or calling a professional service technician, and

2) The repair is likely to yield a machine that will operate satisfactorily for several more years, or at least long enough to justify the cost.

In certain parts of the book, the author expresses an opinion as to whether the current value of a particular machine warrants making the repair or "scrapping" the machine. Such opinions are to be construed as opinions ONLY and they are NOT to be construed as legal advice. The decision as to whether to take a particular machine out of service depends on a number of factors that the author cannot possibly know and has no control over; therefore, the responsibility for such a decision rests solely with the person making the decision.

I'm sure that a physicist or a thermodynamicist reading this book could have a lot of fun tearing it apart because of my deliberate avoidance and misuse of technical terms. However, this manual is written to simplify the material and inform the novice, not to appease the scientist.

*NOTE: The diagnosis and repair procedures in this manual do not necessarily apply to brand-new units, newly-installed units or recently relocated units. Although they **may** posess the problems described in this manual, refrigerators that have recently been installed or moved are subject to special considerations not taken into account in this manual for the sake of simplicity. Such special considerations include installation parameters, installation location, the possibility of manufacturing or construction defects, damage in transit, and others.*

This manual was designed to assist the novice technician in the repair of home (domestic) refrigerators that have been operating successfully for an extended period of months or years and have only recently stopped operating properly, with no major change in installation parameters or location.

There is only one exception to this rule; see section 7-4.

Table of Contents

Chapter 1

REFRIGERATION SYSTEM BASICS

1-1. HEAT FLOW AND AIR FLOW

In thinking about the way your refrigerator keeps things cool, there are a few seat-of-the-pants thermodynamic laws that you need to consider:

1) *Don't think of your refrigerator as MAKING THINGS COLD. Think of it as REMOVING HEAT from whatever you put in it.*

2) *Remember that heat always flows* **from** *something of a* **higher** *temperature* **to** *something of a* **lower** *temperature. The greater the temperature difference, the faster the heat flow.*

3) *Heat will continue to flow* **from** *the* **warm**er *object* **to** *the* **cold**er *object until their temperatures are equal.*

Thus, when you put warm food into a cold refrigerator, heat starts flowing from the warm food into the cold air around it. The food starts to get cooler. (The temperature goes down.)

Since the air inside the fridge has now absorbed some heat and is warmer than it should be, we need to carry it away from the food, replace it with new cold air and remove the excess heat from it. This is

why airflow is so important inside the fridge.

A fan is provided inside the fridge to continually circulate internal air. It draws in warm air from all sections of your refrigerator and blows it across the **EVAPORATOR,** or **"COOLING COILS."** This fan is called the **EVAPORATOR FAN.**

As the air flows across the *out*side of the evaporator, it gives up its excess heat to Freon circulating *in*side the evaporator. The Freon in the evaporator runs at a very cold temperature, somewhere between about 9 and 40 degrees below zero, so that the heat will flow out of the air and into the Freon very quickly.

1-2. DEFROST SYSTEM

However, when you opened that door to put the food into the fridge, you also let in a big charge of warm, relatively moist (humid) air. The evaporator is SO cold that the humidity from the air will freeze directly onto it, creating **FROST.** If enough frost builds up on the evaporator, air will not be able to flow across it.

To prevent too much frost from collecting on the evaporator coils, a self-defrosting refrigerator will actually stop itself for a few minutes every six to twelve hours or so, and melt its own frost. How often this "defrost cycle" occurs, and how long it lasts, is controlled by a motor-driven mechanical **DEFROST TIMER,** or by an electronic "computer board" called an **ADC** (**Adaptive Defrost Control**.) The timer or ADC stops the compressor (cooling system) and starts an electric **DEFROST HEATER** located directly beneath the evaporator coils. The heat rises and melts the frost.

The frost water is drained away, usually to the little pan that you see beneath your refrigerator in most models. Eventually it will evaporate away. If all the frost melts before the defrost timer finishes the defrost cycle, a **TERMINATING THERMOSTAT** will keep the defrost heater from overheating the evaporator compartment. It is wired in series with the heater. When the compartment reaches a certain temperature, the terminating thermostat will open and shut off the defrost heater.

1-3. TEMPERATURE CONTROL

As the food in the fridge gets colder, it gives off less heat, and the air inside the fridge will remain colder. A thermostat called a **COLD CONTROL** will cycle the cooling system on and off to keep the temperature inside your fridge within a certain range. You can adjust that range using one of the dials within your fridge.

On most fridges, all the cold air for both the food compartment and the freezer compartment is produced in one evaporator. Since the freezer is so much colder than the food compartment, most of the cold air that is produced circulates to the freezer compartment. Only a small amount is needed in the food compartment to keep it down to the proper temperature. This amount is adjusted by a small **AIR DOOR** in the duct between the evaporator and the food compartment. The control for this air door is the other of the two dials within your fridge.

1-4. WHERE DOES THE HEAT GO?

In order to re-use the Freon for cooling more air, the heat that WAS in your food and is NOW in your Freon must somehow be gotten rid of. The Freon gas goes to the **COMPRESSOR** where it is compressed into a hot gas (remember, when you compress a gas, it gets warmer.) The Freon then flows through the **CONDENSER**, which is the warm grille you'll find either behind or underneath your refrigerator. It resembles the radiator in your car and acts in much the same manner. The heat from your food, plus whatever heat was added during compression, will flow *from* the hot Freon in your condenser *to* the cooler air in your kitchen.

In some models a **CONDENSER FAN** is fitted to circulate air across the condenser. Air circulation is very important to heat flow. On some models, the warmth from the condenser is used to evaporate the defrost water. That's also the source of the warm air you might feel blowing out from beneath your fridge while it is running.

After the Freon loses the excess heat in the condenser, it is de-compressed, or expanded, by simply putting it through a constriction that lets the pressure drop. This readies the Freon to go through the evaporator again, and the cycle begins all over.

Chapter 2

SPECIAL TYPES OF REFRIGERATORS

A vast majority of the refrigerators built within the last 30-40 years (and thus most likely to still be in service) were built using the systems described in Chapter 1; however, there are a few exceptions:

2-1. HOT GAS DEFROST

Certain refrigerators use hot Freon circulated backwards through the evaporator to melt frost, rather than an electric heater. Though there *are* more recent models, these are generally built in the 1960's and before and represent a very small minority of the domestic refrigerators still in service.

2-2. NON SELF-DEFROSTERS

These units do not have a timer that initiates the defrost mode. Some must be initiated manually (usually there is an obvious defrost button) and some have no defrost at all—they must be unloaded, unplugged, and let defrost by themselves.

2-3. CHILL-TYPE REFRIGERATORS

These refrigerators have a very cold plate or coils (tubes) located near the top of the cold compartment. There is no evaporator fan and air circulates naturally. By convection, warm air rises to the top of the compartment where the coils are, and the cold air sinks towards the bottom.

There may be separate plates in the freezer and refrigerator sections. Often these refrigerators have no defrost systems; if they do, it's usually a hot-gas defrost system. Most "micro-" or "mini-" fridges are chill-type. Most freezer (only) units have no evaporator fans. Generally these units have no condenser fan either; condenser air circulation is also by convection.

2-4. GAS REFRIGERATORS (AMMONIA SYSTEMS)

IF YOU HAVE A "GAS" REFRIGERATOR, NOTHING IN THIS BOOK APPLIES TO YOUR UNIT. It uses an entirely different operating system; it is NOT a vapor-compression-cycle unit. These are generally found in RV and yacht installations, where electricity is frequently unavailable for extended periods of time.

If you suspect that you may have any of these units, ask your appliance parts retailer or dealer to confirm your suspicions. (See Section 3-1; "BEFORE YOU START.") With a make, a model number and perhaps a serial number, he should be able to tell you what you have.

Chapter 3

DIAGNOSIS AND REPAIR BASICS

3-1(a) "GREEN" PLUGS

DON'T use them on refrigerators. "Green" plugs usually work fine on resistive loads such as heaters and incandescent lights. But in my opinion, you should not use them on electronics, and things that are motorized. These things are made to operate on electricity with certain "waveform" characteristics. A "green" plug modifies those characteristics; you are asking for trouble.

Refrigerators have SEVERAL motors in them, and modern refrigerators have electronic components, too. Green plugs have caused all kinds of problems in fridges, such as moisture buildup due to slower fan speeds, and compressor starting and heating problems.

Equally importantly, a 'green' plug might VOID THE WARRANTY on your fridge.

Because of government-mandated efficiency requirements, modern refrigerators already have a great energy-saving features built into them. You don't need a green plug on a fridge...don't use them!

3-1(b) BEFORE YOU START

Find yourself a good appliance parts dealer. You can find them in the Yellow Pages under the following headings:

● APPLIANCES, HOUSEHOLD, MAJOR
● APPLIANCES, PARTS AND SUPPLIES
● REFRIGERATORS, DOMESTIC
● APPLIANCES, HOUSEHOLD, REPAIR AND SERVICE

Call a few of them and ask if they are a repair service, or if they sell parts, or both. Ask them if they offer free advice with the parts they sell. (Occasionally, stores that offer both parts and service will not want to give you advice.) Often, the parts counter men are ex-technicians who got tired of the pressures of going into stressed-out peoples' houses and fixing appliances. They can be your best friends; however, you don't want to badger them with TOO many questions, so know your basics before you start asking questions.

Some parts houses may offer service too. Be careful! They may try to talk you out of even *trying* to fix your own refrigerator. They'll tell you it's too complicated, then in the same breath, "guide" you to their service department. Who are you gonna believe, me or them? Not all service/parts places are this way, however. If they genuinely *try* to help you fix it yourself and you find that you can't fix the problem, they may be a really good place to look for service. Think about it—if they sold you this book, then they're genuinely interested in helping do-it-yourselfers!

When you go into the store, have ready your make, model and serial number from the *nameplate* of the fridge (not from some sticker inside the fridge). If there is a B/M number on the nameplate, have that with you, too.

NAMEPLATE INFORMATION

The metal nameplate information is usually found in one of the places shown in Figure 1:

A) Along the bottom panel; left, right or anywhere in-between.

B) Inside the fridge or freezer section, near the bottom. You may have to remove a crisper drawer to see it.

C) Remove the kickplate and look along the condenser air openings.

D) Somewhere on the back of the refrigerator, usually very high or very low, or possibly on any wiring diagram that may be pasted to the back of the refrigerator.

E) If you absolutely cannot find a metal nameplate, some refrigerators have a paper sales sticker left on, just inside the door. This will be an incomplete model number, but it is better than nothing and it should be good enough to get most parts with.

If all else fails, check the original papers that came with your fridge when it was new. They should contain the model number SOMEWHERE.

If you have absolutely NO information about the fridge anywhere, make sure you bring your old part to the parts store with you. Sometimes they can match an old part by looks or by part number.

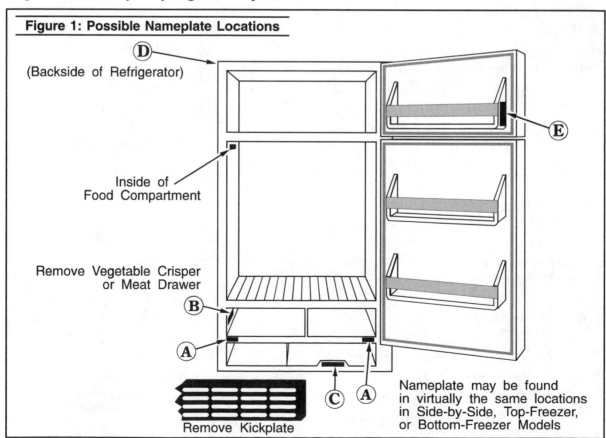

Figure 1: Possible Nameplate Locations

(Backside of Refrigerator)

Inside of Food Compartment

Remove Vegetable Crisper or Meat Drawer

Remove Kickplate

Nameplate may be found in virtually the same locations in Side-by-Side, Top-Freezer, or Bottom-Freezer Models

3-2. TOOLS (Figure 2)

The tools that you will probably need are listed below. Some are optional. The reason for the option is explained.

SCREWDRIVERS: Both flat and phillips head; two or three different sizes of each. It is best to have at least a stubby, 4" and 6" sizes.

NUTDRIVERS: You will need at least a 1/4" and a 5/16" nut driver. 4 or 6" ones should suffice, but it's better to have stubbies, too.

BLOW DRYER and **SYRINGE TYPE TURKEY BASTER:** For manually melting frost and ice.

ALLIGATOR JUMPERS (sometimes called a **"CHEATER"** or **"CHEATER WIRE"**): small gauge (14-16 gauge or so) and about 12 to 18 inches long; for testing electrical circuits. Available at your local electronics store. Cost: a few bucks for 4 or 5 of them.

ELECTRICAL PLIERS or **STRIPPERS** and **DIAGONAL CUTTING PLIERS:** For cutting and stripping small electrical wire.

BUTT CONNECTORS, CRIMPERS, WIRE NUTS AND ELECTRICAL TAPE: For splicing small wire.

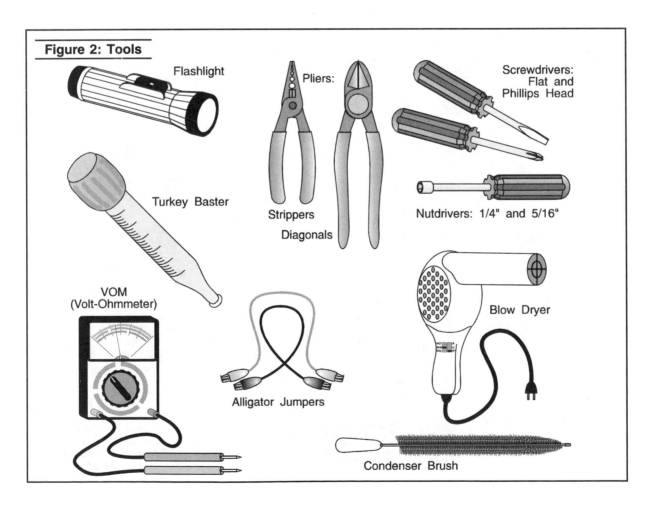

Figure 2: Tools

Flashlight

Pliers:

Strippers

Diagonals

Screwdrivers: Flat and Phillips Head

Turkey Baster

Nutdrivers: 1/4" and 5/16"

VOM (Volt-Ohmmeter)

Alligator Jumpers

Blow Dryer

Condenser Brush

FLASHLIGHT: For obvious reasons.

VOM(VOLT-OHM METER): For testing circuits. If you do not have one, get one. An inexpensive one will suffice, as long as it has both "A.C. Voltage" and "Resistance" (i.e. R x 1, R x 10, etc.) settings on the dial. It will do for our purposes. If you are inexperienced in using one, get an analog (pointer) type (as opposed to a digital.)

CONDENSER BRUSH: For cleaning out that dusty "black hole" beneath your fridge, otherwise known as your condenser. It is a long, stiff-bristled brush especially made for knocking out massive wads of dust from your condenser grille. I have seen jury-rigged bottle brushes and vacuums used, neither of which clean sufficiently. C'mon—buy the right tool for the job. They're cheap enough.

OPTIONAL TOOLS (Figure 3)

SNAP-AROUND AMMETER: For determining if electrical components are energized. Quite useful; but a bit expensive, and there are alternative methods. If you have one, use it; otherwise, don't bother getting one.

EXTENDIBLE INSPECTION MIRROR: For seeing difficult places beneath the refrigerator and behind panels.

CORDLESS POWER SCREWDRIVER OR DRILL/DRIVER WITH MAGNETIC SCREWDRIVER AND NUTDRIVER TIPS: For pulling off panels held in place by many screws. It can save you lots of time and hassle.

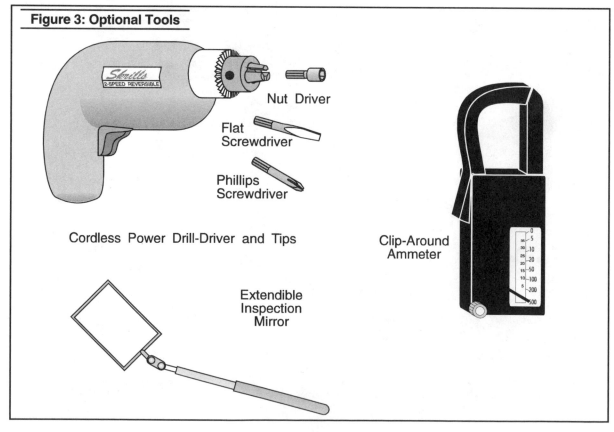

Figure 3: Optional Tools

Nut Driver

Flat Screwdriver

Phillips Screwdriver

Cordless Power Drill-Driver and Tips

Clip-Around Ammeter

Extendible Inspection Mirror

3-3 HOW TO USE A VOM AND AMMETER

Many home handymen are very intimidated by electricity. It's true that diagnosing and repairing electrical circuits requires a *bit* more care than most operations, due to the danger of getting shocked. But there is no mystery or voodoo about the things we'll be doing. Remember the rule in section 3-4 (1); while you are working on a circuit, energize the circuit only long enough to perform whatever test you're performing, then take the power back off it to perform the repair. You need not be concerned with any theory, like what an ohm is, or what a volt is. You will only need to be able to set the VOM onto the right scale, touch the test leads to the right place and read the meter.

In using the VOM (Volt-Ohm Meter) for our purposes, the two test leads are always plugged into the "+" and "-" holes on the VOM. (Some VOMs have more than two holes.)

3-3(a) TESTING VOLTAGE (Figure 4)

Set the VOM's dial on the lowest VAC scale (A.C. Voltage) that's over 120 volts. For example, if there's a 50 setting and a 250 setting on the VAC dial, use the 250 scale, because 250 is the lowest setting over 120 volts.

Touch the two test leads to the two metal contacts of a live power source, like a wall outlet or the terminals of the motor that you're testing for voltage. (*Do not* **jam** *the test leads into a wall outlet!*) If you are getting power through the VOM, the meter will jump up and steady on a reading. You *may* have to convert the scale in your head. For example, if you're using the 250 volt dial setting and the meter has a "25" scale, simply divide by 10; 120 volts would be "12" on the meter.

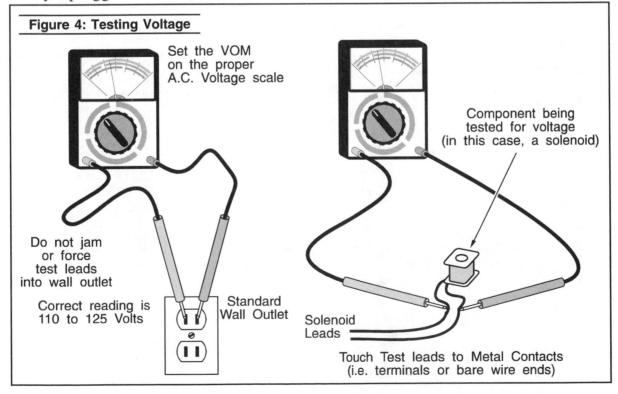

Figure 4: Testing Voltage

Set the VOM on the proper A.C. Voltage scale

Do not jam or force test leads into wall outlet

Correct reading is 110 to 125 Volts

Standard Wall Outlet

Component being tested for voltage (in this case, a solenoid)

Solenoid Leads

Touch Test leads to Metal Contacts (i.e. terminals or bare wire ends)

3-3(b) TESTING FOR CONTINUITY AND RESISTANCE (Figure 5)

Don't let the word "continuity" scare you. It's derived from the word "continuous." In an electrical circuit, electricity has to flow *from* a power source back *to* that power source. If there is any break in the circuit, it is not continuous, and it has no continuity. "Good" continuity means that there is no break in the circuit.

For example, if you were testing a heater element to see if it was burned out, you would try putting a small amount of power through the heater. If the heater element was burned out, there would be a break in the circuit, the electricity wouldn't flow, and your meter would show no continuity.

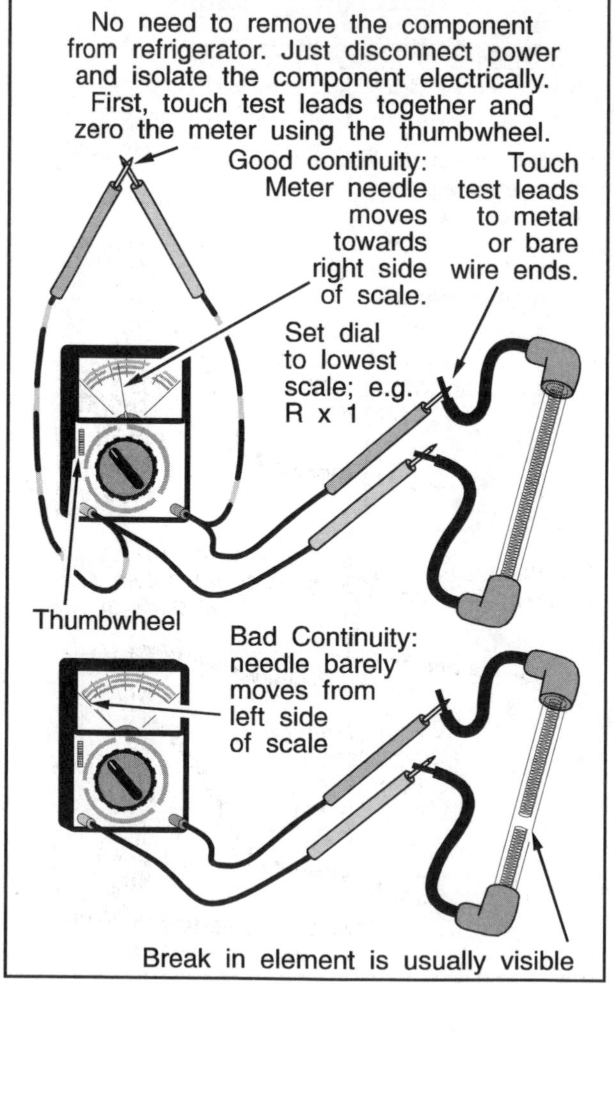

That is what the *resistance* part of your VOM does; it provides a small electrical current (using batteries within the VOM) and measures how fast the current is flowing. The current flow is measured in Ohms; the more resistance that there *is* to current flow, the more Ohms your meter will read.

To use your VOM to test continuity, set the dial on (resistance) R x 1, R x 10, or whatever the *lowest* setting is. Touch the metal parts of the test leads together and read the meter. It should peg the meter all the way on the right side of the scale, towards "0" on the meter's "resistance" scale. If the meter does not read zero resistance, adjust the thumbwheel on the front of the VOM until it *does* read zero. If you cannot get the meter to read zero, the battery in the VOM is low; replace it.

If you are testing, say, a heater, first make sure that the heater leads are not connected to *anything*, *especially* a power source. If the heater's leads are still connected to something, you *may* get a reading through that something. If there is still live power on the item you're testing for continuity, you will burn out your VOM in microseconds and possibly shock yourself.

Touch the two test leads to the two bare wire ends or terminals of the heater. You can touch the ends of the wires and test leads with your hands if necessary to get better contact. The voltage that the VOM batteries put out is very low, and you will not be shocked. If there is NO continuity, the meter won't move. If there is GOOD continuity, the meter will move toward the right side of the scale

Figure 5: Testing for Continuity

No need to remove the component from refrigerator. Just disconnect power and isolate the component electrically. First, touch test leads together and zero the meter using the thumbwheel.

Good continuity: Meter needle moves towards right side of scale.

Touch test leads to metal or bare wire ends.

Set dial to lowest scale; e.g. R x 1

Thumbwheel

Bad Continuity: needle barely moves from left side of scale

Break in element is usually visible

and steady on a reading. This is the resistance reading. Most of the time this doesn't concern us; we only care that we show good continuity. If the meter moves only very little and stays towards the left side of the scale, that's BAD continuity; the heater is no good. In a glass-tube or bare-element heater, you *may* be able to see the physical break in the heater element, just like you can in some light bulbs.

If you are testing a switch or a thermostat, you will show little or no resistance (good continuity) when the switch or thermostat is closed, and NO continuity when the switch is open. If you do not, the switch is bad.

3-3(c) AMMETERS

Ammeters are a little bit more complex to explain without going into a lot of electrical theory. If you own an ammeter, you probably already know how to use it.

If you don't, don't get one. Ammeters are expensive. And for *our* purposes, there are other ways to determine what an ammeter tests for. If you don't own one, skip this section.

For our purposes, ammeters are simply a way of testing for continuity without having to cut into the system or to disconnect power from whatever it is we're testing.

Ammeters measure the current in amps flowing through a wire. The greater the current that's flowing *through* a wire, the greater the magnetic field it produces *around* the wire. The ammeter simply measures this magnetic field, and thus the amount of current, flowing through

the wire. To determine continuity, for our purposes, we can simply isolate the component that we're testing (so we do not accidentally measure the current going through any other components) and see if there's *any* current flow.

To use your ammeter, first make sure that it's on an appropriate scale (0 to 10 or 20 amps will do). Isolate a wire leading directly to the component you're testing. Put the ammeter loop around that wire and read the meter. (Figure 6)

What if that you have trouble finding the wire lead to, say, a defrost heater that you're testing, because the wires are frozen into a block of ice?

If you isolate all systems so the heater

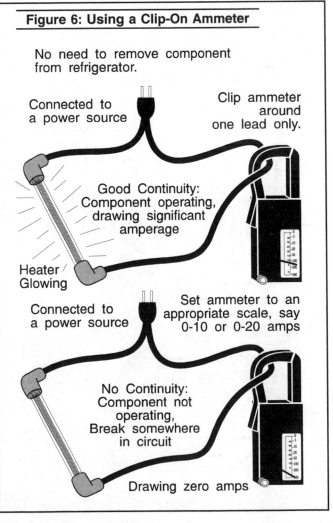

Figure 6: Using a Clip-On Ammeter

No need to remove component from refrigerator.

Connected to a power source

Clip ammeter around one lead only.

Good Continuity: Component operating, drawing significant amperage

Heater Glowing

Connected to a power source

Set ammeter to an appropriate scale, say 0-10 or 0-20 amps

No Continuity: Component not operating, Break somewhere in circuit

Drawing zero amps

is the only thing energized, then you can test the easily accessible main power cord for current, and it must be the current being used by the heater.

This is relatively easy to do. Turn the "energy saver" switch to the "economy" position to shut off the anti-sweat mullion heaters (See section 4-1.) Close the refrigerator door to make sure the lights are off. Set the defrost timer to the defrost mode. This will stop the compressor, and energize the defrost heater (*if* it is working; *that*, of course, is what we're testing.) Remove the lower back panel of the fridge and find where the main power cord branches off in two directions. (See Figure 7) Test one lead (*one* lead *only*) for current flow. There may still be a tiny mullion heater energized in the butter conditioner or on the defrost drain pan, but the current that these heaters draw is negligible for our purposes (less than an amp). If you have *any* substantial current flow, it's *got* to be through the defrost heater. If you don't, the defrost heater or terminating thermostat is probably defective.

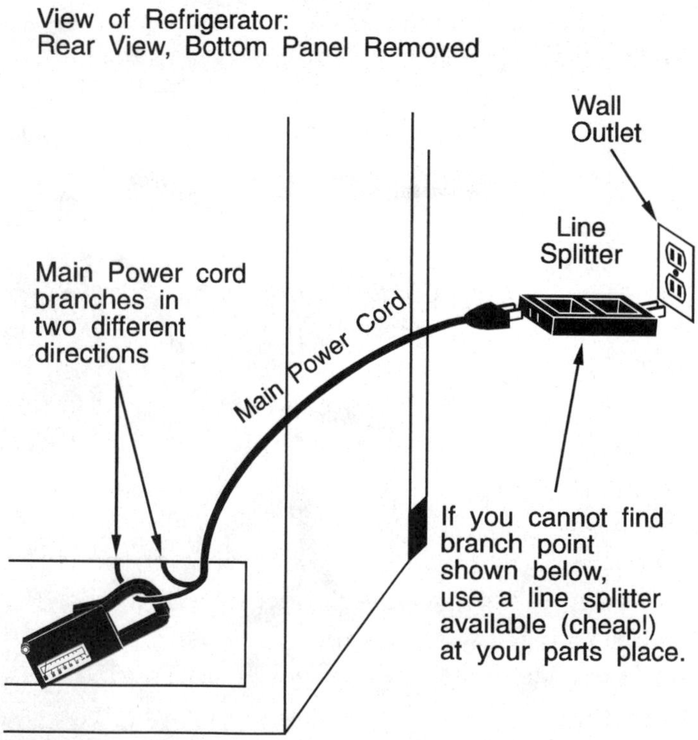

3-4. BASIC REPAIR AND SAFETY PRECAUTIONS

1) Always de-energize (pull the plug or trip the breaker on) any refrigerator that you're disassembling. If you need to re-energize the refrigerator to perform a test, make sure any bare wires or terminals are taped or insulated. Energize the unit only long enough to perform whatever test you're performing, then disconnect the power again.

2) **_NEVER EVER_** chip or dig out ice from around the evaporator with a sharp instrument or knife. You WILL PROBABLY puncture the evaporator and you WILL PROBABLY end up buying a new refrigerator. Use hot water and/or a blow dryer to melt ice. If you use a

Figure 7: Testing Amps in the Main Power Line

View of Refrigerator:
Rear View, Bottom Panel Removed

Main Power cord branches in two different directions

Main Power Cord

Wall Outlet

Line Splitter

If you cannot find branch point shown below, use a line splitter available (cheap!) at your parts place.

blow dryer, take care not to get water in it and shock yourself. Better yet, if you have the time and patience, leave the fridge open for a few hours and let the ice melt naturally. You can remove large, loose chunks of ice in the evaporator compartment by hand, but make sure there aren't any electrical wires frozen into the chunks of ice before you start pulling them.

3) Always re-install any removed duck seal, heat shields, styrofoam insulation, or panels that you remove to access *anything*. They're there for a reason.

4) You may need to empty your fridge or freezer for an operation. If you do not have another fridge (or a friend with one) to keep your food in, you can generally get by with an ice chest or a cardboard box insulated with towels for a short time. Never re-freeze meats; if they've already thawed, cook them and use them later.

5) If this manual advocates replacing a part, REPLACE IT!! You might find, say, a fan motor that has stopped for no apparent reason. Sometimes you can flip it with your finger and get it going again. The key words here are *apparent reason*. There is a reason that it stopped—you can bet on it—and if you get it going and re-install it, you are running a very high risk that it will stop again. If *that* happens, you will have to start repairing your refrigerator *all* over again. There may be a hard spot in the bearings; or it may only act up when it is hot, or cold...there are a hundred different "what if's." Very few, if any,

of the parts mentioned in this book will cost you over ten or twenty dollars. Don't be penny-wise and dollar-dumb. Replace the part.

6) Refrigerator defrost problems may take a week or more to reappear if you don't fix the problem the first time. That's how long it will take the evaporator to build up enough frost to block the airflow again. After fixing a defrost problem, keep an eye out for signs of a recurrence for at least a week. The sooner you catch it, the less ice you'll have to melt.

7) You may stop the compressor from running using the defrost timer or cold control, by cutting off the power to the fridge, or simply by pulling the plug out of the wall. However, if you try to re-start it within a few minutes, it *may* not start; you may hear buzzing and clicking noises. (See section 5-3(e)). If the system has not had enough time for the pressure within to equalize, there will be too much back pressure in the system for the compressor motor to overcome when trying to start. This is nothing to be alarmed about. Simply remove the power from the compressor for a few more minutes until the compressor *will* restart.

8) Do not lubricate any of the timers or motors mentioned in this manual. They are permanently self-lubricated. In a cold environment, oil will become more viscous and *increase* friction, rather than decrease it. If you have a sticky fan motor or timer, replace it.

Chapter 4 Overview

Step-by-Step

Complaint: Warm refrigerator, or not as cold as usual
Chapter Qualifier: Compressor is running

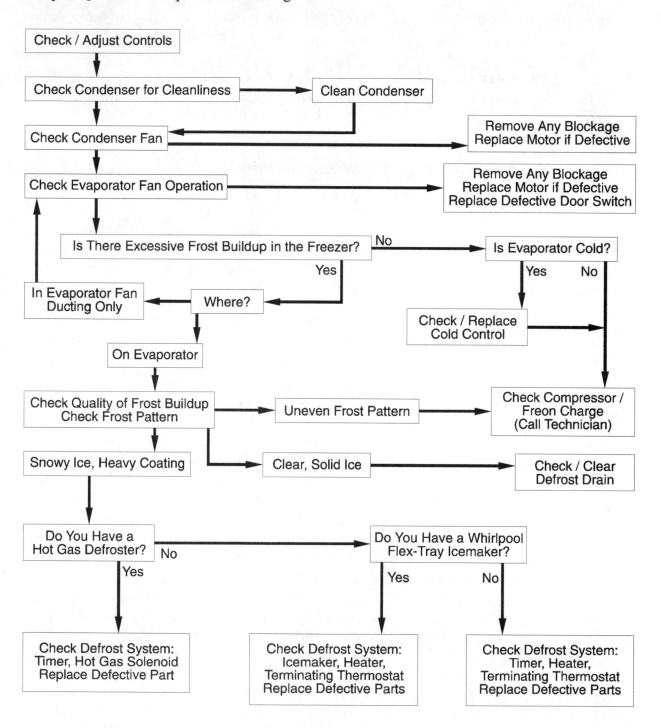

Chapter 4

COMPRESSOR IS RUNNING
BUT REFRIGERATOR IS NOT COLD

Before you perform any of the other tests in this chapter, make sure that the compressor is running. If it is *not* running, see Chapter 5.

Some refrigerators are very quiet and smooth when they operate. If you cannot hear your refrigerator running or feel the compressor vibrating, you must investigate further.

First, try turning the cold control to the "off" position or unplugging the fridge; this will stop the compressor. Do you hear or feel a difference? If so, the compressor *was* running. WAIT SEVERAL MINUTES before turning the compressor back on for your diagnostic checks. The reason for waiting before you restart it is explained in section 3-4 (7).

If you perform the above test and do not feel a difference, try "listening with a screwdriver." Access the compressor by opening the back panel and place the metal end of a long screwdriver against the compressor and your ear against the plastic end of the screwdriver. You should hear the compressor running. If you are still unsure and you own an am-

meter, test the current draw of the compressor at the compressor leads. If the compressor is running, it should draw about **6** amps.

4-1 CONTROLS

If your compressor is running and your refrigerator is warm in both compartments (or not as cold as usual, i.e. chilly but meats are thawing,) first check your CONTROLS. You never know if your kids got in there and messed around with them. Set them on mid-range settings. See section 7-1 on KID CAPERS for some interesting stories about this subject.

Inside either the freezer or refrigerator compartment you will generally find at least two dial type controls.

One of them, called the cold control, is an electric switch that starts and stops the compressor based on the temperature that it senses inside the compartment.

The other dial is an air door that controls the small amount of air that passes to the food compartment while the evaporator fan is running. (See Section 1-3)

In some refrigerators, the movement of these air doors is not manually controlled. They may be controlled thermomechanically, or even electrically, by a computer board such as the ADC (Adaptive Defrost Control.) But there is usually a knob for setting the temperature that you want in each compartment.

Either dial may be marked with any one of a dozen different labels: "refrigerator control," "freezer control," "food compartment control," etc. Determining which is which can get a bit confusing. If the knob has an "off" setting which stops the compressor from running, it is the *cold control.*

In the absence of an "off" setting, the easiest way to tell them apart is to pull the plastic knob off the control. The *cold control* will usually have a wide tang and a narrow tang. (See Figure 8) The *air door* will usually have a plastic or metal "D"-shaped shaft (a round shaft with a flat) to which it attaches, although this is not always the case.

If one dial is in the freezer section and one is in the food section, the one in the *freezer* section is the *cold control*, and the one in the *food* section is the *air door*.

If the knobs will not come off with a firm pull, or you are still unsure of which control is which, try putting your hand in front of the air vents in the food compartment and manipulating the controls. Make sure the evap fan is running; you *may* have to *tape* the door switch so it stays on. If you are manipulating the air door, there should be a detectable difference in the strength of the air draft from the low setting to the high setting.

Often, the first thing that folks do when their refrigerator starts to feel warm is turn both controls on the coldest settings. **This is exactly the WRONG thing to do**. Turning the cold

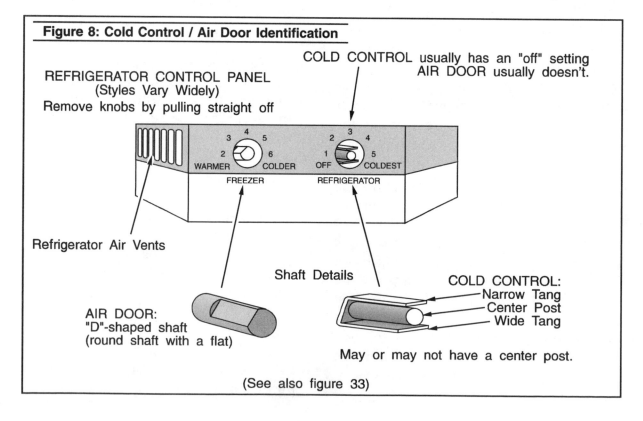

Figure 8: Cold Control / Air Door Identification

REFRIGERATOR CONTROL PANEL
(Styles Vary Widely)
Remove knobs by pulling straight off

COLD CONTROL usually has an "off" setting
AIR DOOR usually doesn't.

WARMER   COLDER   OFF   COLDEST
FREEZER   REFRIGERATOR

Refrigerator Air Vents

AIR DOOR:
"D"-shaped shaft
(round shaft with a flat)

Shaft Details

COLD CONTROL:
Narrow Tang
Center Post
Wide Tang

May or may not have a center post.

(See also figure 33)

control to the coldest setting *will* keep the compressor running longer and make lots of cold air. But turning the air door to the coldest setting *closes* the airway to the food section. Lots of cold air is made, but most of it stays in the freezer section, and the food section actually gets *warmer*.

OTHER CONTROLS:
"VEGETABLE" OR "MEAT" COMPARTMENT CONTROLS BUTTER CONDITIONER, ENERGY SAVER

VEGETABLE (CRISPER) or MEAT COMPARTMENT CONTROLS:
These may be small heaters or they may be separate air doors that control the airflow within these compartments. The idea is to keep the compartment at a different temperature from the rest of the food compartment; a more optimum temperature for the particular food that you're keeping in these compartments. Certain high-end fridges are even using thermistor-controlled air

doors, and some pretty exotic technologies such as semi-permeable membranes to control humidity in these compartments.

BUTTER CONDITIONERS:
Again, small heaters that keep the butter compartment at a different temperature than the rest of the food compartment.

"ENERGY SAVER" OR EFFICIENCY SWITCHES:
If you live in a warm, humid environment, you may have a problem with condensation forming on the *outside* of your refrigerator. This is known as "sweating." So-called "Energy Saver" switches control small, low-wattage "mullion" heaters in the side and door panels that prevent the outside of the refrigerator from getting cool enough for sweating to occur. In the "economy" position, the heaters are *off*.

If the refrigerator has cooling problems, often the first symptom will be that the mullions start to feel warm.

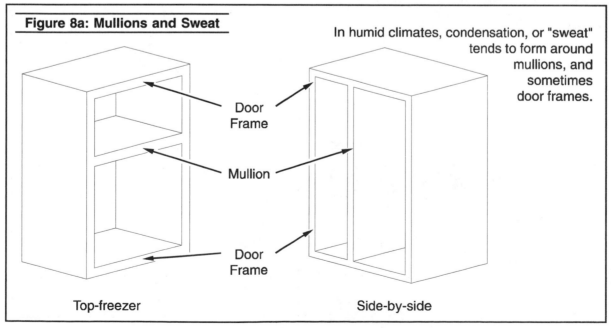

Figure 8a: Mullions and Sweat

In humid climates, condensation, or "sweat" tends to form around mullions, and sometimes door frames.

Door Frame

Mullion

Door Frame

Top-freezer

Side-by-side

4-2. CONDENSER AND CONDENSER FAN

Next, check your condenser and condenser fan.

The locations of the most common types of condensers are shown in Figures 9A, 9B & 10. Any type condenser mount may be used on bottom-freezer, top-freezer or side-by-side units.

FIGURE 9A: A back-mounted condenser has no condenser fan. Air flows over it by convection; the warm air rises and is replaced by cooler air from below. Some of these condensers are covered by a metal plate.

FIGURE 9B: Bottom-mounted condensers come in many configurations. Most look like a radiator or grille beneath the fridge, behind the kickplate. They are accessible for cleaning through the bottom front of the refrigerator. A condenser fan moves air across these condensers.

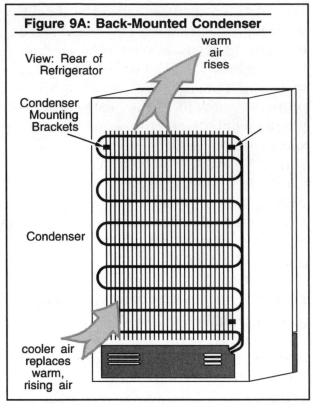

Figure 9A: Back-Mounted Condenser

View: Rear of Refrigerator

warm air rises

Condenser Mounting Brackets

Condenser

cooler air replaces warm, rising air

FIGURE 10: Another fairly common type of bottom-mount condenser is wrapped in a metal plate and is accessible through the bottom back panel of the refrigerator.

The condenser *fan* may be mounted in a number of different ways. Usually it is accessed by removing the bottom back panel. Figures 10 & 11 show the most common arrangement for the condenser fan.

DIAGNOSIS AND REPAIR

If you have a back-condenser refrigerator, make sure that nothing has fallen behind your fridge that might block the airflow.

If you have a bottom condenser, remove the baseplate (kickplate) from the bottom front of the refrigerator and look beneath it with a powerful flashlight. If you have kids or dogs or if

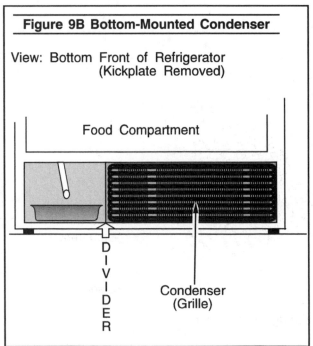

Figure 9B Bottom-Mounted Condenser

View: Bottom Front of Refrigerator (Kickplate Removed)

Food Compartment

DIVIDER

Condenser (Grille)

your clothes dryer is installed nearby, you are a prime candidate to have a blocked condenser. Quite a bit of dust is normal; still, enough may be impacted to block the airflow completely. Feel for a steady flow of warm air from the drain pan side; it should be obvious (see Figure 11). Clean your condenser with a condenser brush. (*NOTE: Some condensers must be accessed through the back panel.*)

CAUTION: When cleaning your condenser, you want to do it thoroughly, but don't be too vigorous about it. You don't want to knock loose any wiring beneath the fridge. Also, you may hit the condenser fan (with a grinding thud) with the brush. Don't worry too much about it; you probably won't hurt the fan or motor, though it is something you want to avoid if possible.

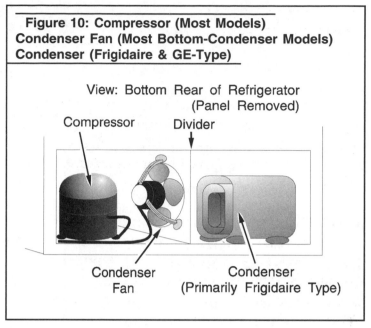

Figure 10: Compressor (Most Models)
Condenser Fan (Most Bottom-Condenser Models)
Condenser (Frigidaire & GE-Type)

View: Bottom Rear of Refrigerator
(Panel Removed)

Compressor   Divider

Condenser
Fan

Condenser
(Primarily Frigidaire Type)

If the airflow improves dramatically, then that may have been your only problem.

After you clean your condenser, pull the lower back panel off the fridge. Make sure that the condenser fan is running and not blocked by any loose insulation or other objects.

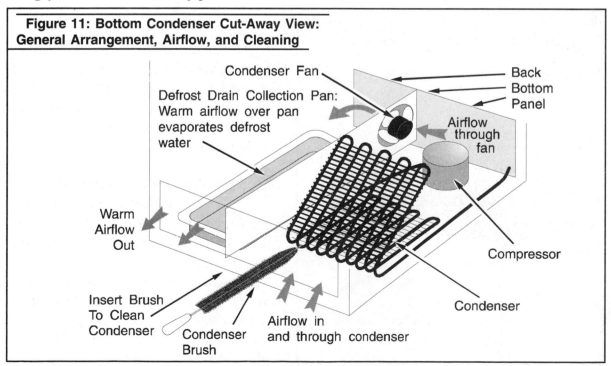

Figure 11: Bottom Condenser Cut-Away View:
General Arrangement, Airflow, and Cleaning

Condenser Fan

Defrost Drain Collection Pan:
Warm airflow over pan
evaporates defrost
water

Back
Bottom
Panel

Airflow
through
fan

Warm
Airflow
Out

Compressor

Insert Brush
To Clean
Condenser

Condenser
Brush

Airflow in
and through condenser

Condenser

MAKE SURE THAT YOU RE-PLACE THE BACK BOTTOM PANEL!!! If it is missing, fashion one out of a piece out of corrugated cardboard and screw it on using the existing screwholes. It has the *very important* job of directing airflow beneath the fridge, assuring that the condenser fan is drawing air over the condenser and not just sucking air in through the back of the fridge. (Figure 12)

If the condenser fan is stopped and there is nothing blocking it, replace the fan motor. They are sealed units and cannot be rebuilt.

Replacing the condenser fan motor can be dirty and difficult. There are two types of mounts most commonly used; (Figure 13)

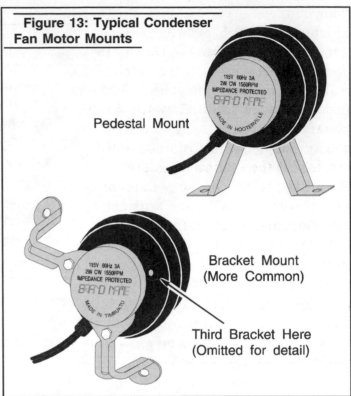

Figure 13: Typical Condenser Fan Motor Mounts

Pedestal Mount

Bracket Mount (More Common)

Third Bracket Here (Omitted for detail)

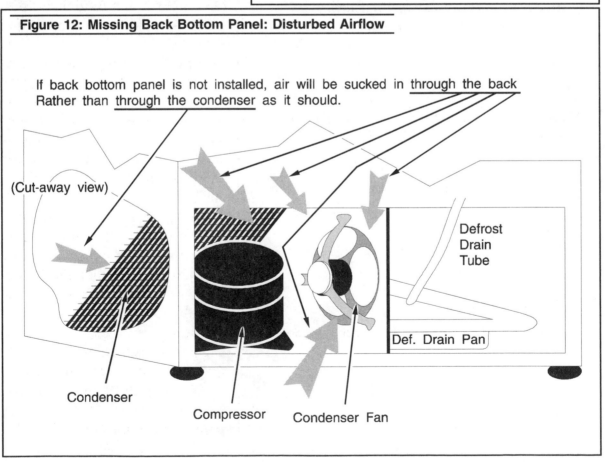

Figure 12: Missing Back Bottom Panel: Disturbed Airflow

If back bottom panel is not installed, air will be sucked in through the back Rather than through the condenser as it should.

(Cut-away view)

Defrost Drain Tube

Def. Drain Pan

Condenser

Compressor

Condenser Fan

bracket mount (the most common) and pedestal mount. It is usually easiest to remove the mounting brackets or pedestal from their place in the refrigerator, with the fan motor attached. When installing a new motor with bracket mounts, it may be easier to install the brackets loosely on the motor until you can locate the mounting screws in their holes. The wires can be cut and re-connected with crimp-on butt connectors or wire nuts and electrical tape.

Even if you find a dirty condenser or stopped condenser fan, it's a good idea to go through the rest of the tests in this chapter to be certain that you've solved your problem.

4-3 EVAPORATOR FAN

On some models, the evaporator fan shuts off via a door switch when you open the refrigerator door. Thus, when trouble-shooting the evaporator fan, you must depress the door switch(es).

Open your freezer door, depress all door switches and listen for the evaporator fan. If you do not hear it running, there's a problem. It might be ice-blocked, or it might have worn out and stopped. The door switch that operates it might be defective. If you *do* hear the evaporator fan running but you do not feel a strong blast of freezing air from the freezer vents, then you probably have a frost problem; see section 4-4.

IF THE EVAPORATOR FAN IS NOT RUNNING, You *may* need to pull off the entire evaporator panel as described in section 4-4 to access the fan. Look first for a separate access panel or a tower within the freezer that houses the fan (Figure 14). Check for anything that may be blocking the fan, including ice from a backed-up defrost drain or a frost problem. If something is blocking the fan, clear it out of the way. If the blockage is due to frost or ice, you must investigate the source and solve the problem.

Depress the door switch. If nothing is blocking the fan and it still does not run, check for voltage across the fan motor leads (with the door switch depressed, of course.)

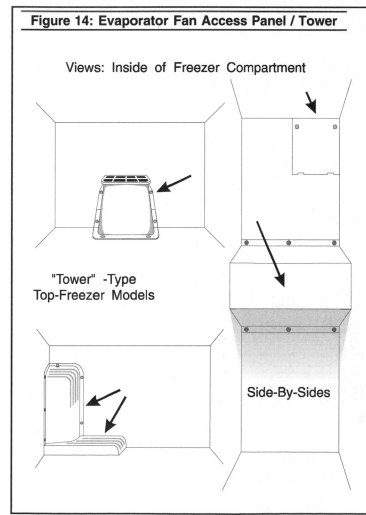

Figure 14: Evaporator Fan Access Panel / Tower

Views: Inside of Freezer Compartment

"Tower" -Type Top-Freezer Models

Side-By-Sides

If you have voltage across the fan motor leads, the fan motor is bad. Replace it.

If you *don't* have voltage to the fan motor, the door switch might be bad. Take power off the fridge and pry out the door switch. You might have to destroy it to get it out. Check for voltage to the switch. If the switch is bad, replace it. (Figure 15).

SLOW-RUNNING EVAPORATOR FAN MOTOR

Sometimes the evap fan will run *slower* than it should. This can be diffi-cult to diagnose. It *can* cause ice to build up in the internal ductwork.

If you hear a "whistling" or "warbling" noise emanating from the fan motor itself or from the inside of the food or freezer compartment, it is probably coming from the evaporator fan motor. The bearings are worn and loose or sticky. Replace the motor.

As I said, a slow evap fan can be very difficult to diagnose. Usually it is done by sound and by experience. The chances are, if it *sounds* slow or strange, it is malfunctioning. Try replacing it. They don't cost much.

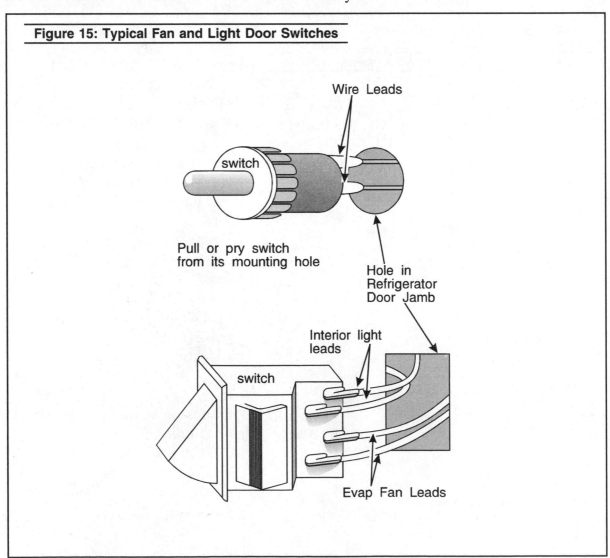

Figure 15: Typical Fan and Light Door Switches

Wire Leads

switch

Pull or pry switch from its mounting hole

Hole in Refrigerator Door Jamb

Interior light leads

switch

Evap Fan Leads

REPLACING THE EVAPORATOR FAN MOTOR

In replacing the fan motor, you must make sure that the rotation of the new fan motor is the same as the old one. The easiest way to do this is to look for the shading poles on the old fan motor (Figure 16). If they are on opposite corners from the ones on the new fan motor core, it is a simple enough task to reverse the new rotor in its core. Carefully remove the bearing cage screws and simply turn the rotor around so the shaft sticks out the other end of the motor.

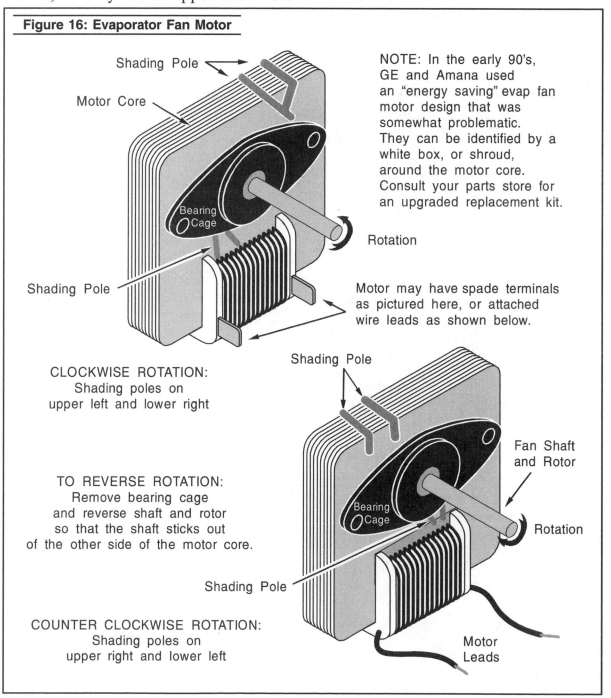

Figure 16: Evaporator Fan Motor

Shading Pole

Motor Core

Bearing Cage

Shading Pole

NOTE: In the early 90's, GE and Amana used an "energy saving" evap fan motor design that was somewhat problematic. They can be identified by a white box, or shroud, around the motor core. Consult your parts store for an upgraded replacement kit.

Rotation

Motor may have spade terminals as pictured here, or attached wire leads as shown below.

CLOCKWISE ROTATION:
Shading poles on
upper left and lower right

TO REVERSE ROTATION:
Remove bearing cage
and reverse shaft and rotor
so that the shaft sticks out
of the other side of the motor core.

COUNTER CLOCKWISE ROTATION:
Shading poles on
upper right and lower left

Shading Pole

Bearing Cage

Shading Pole

Fan Shaft and Rotor

Rotation

Motor Leads

4-4 FROST PROBLEMS

Remove everything from your freezer, including all food and any shelves. Do not remove the icemaker (if installed.)

Look at and feel the panel covering the bottom or back of the freezer compartment. Is it thick with frost?

On top freezer models, are the holes in the top of the food compartment that lead to the evaporator choked with ice?

Is there ice forming on, or lots of water on the ceiling of the food compartment?

If the answer is yes to any of these questions, there's probably a defrost problem.

If you suspect a defrost problem, first remove any icemaker that may be installed. You will see a removable panel covering the entire back or bottom of your freezer compartment. There may be 6 to 10 or more screws holding it on. (Figures 17, 18 & 19) In some units there is a light

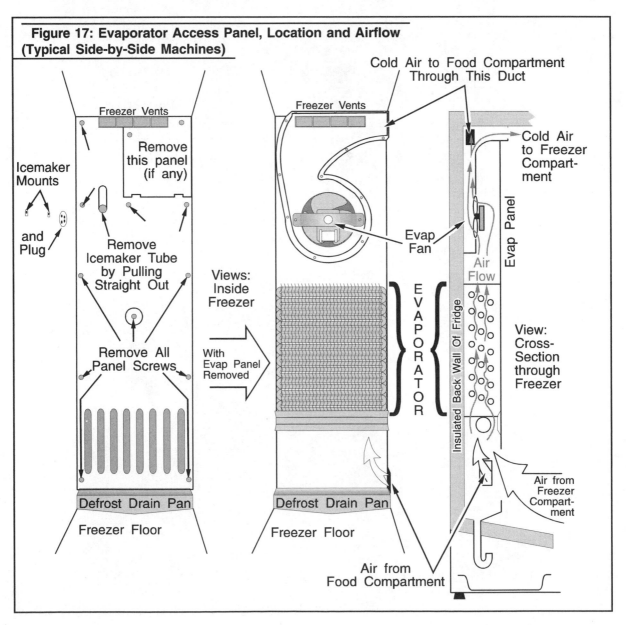

Figure 17: Evaporator Access Panel, Location and Airflow (Typical Side-by-Side Machines)

socket attached to the panel; you'll see this arrangement most often in side-by-sides. These can sometimes be quite difficult to disassemble. Make sure the power is off the refrigerator before disassembling any lighting circuit.

On some bottom-evap models, you may have to remove some of the plastic moulding around the door frame to access some of the evaporator panel screws. (Figure 19) Be extra careful; the plastic moulding can be brittle and break easily. The plastic will bend; just go slow. You may even try heating it a little with a blow dryer, to soften it.

The panel may be frozen to the evaporator; be careful you do not bend or break it. Sometimes it pays to take a few extra minutes and melt the ice a little bit first. This can usually be accomplished by placing a pan of very hot water in various places on the panel, or by blowing warm air on it with a blow-dryer. Do not melt *all* the ice just yet; only enough to get the panel off. You want most of it to remain there at this point so you can further diagnose the problem.

NOTE: The terminating thermostat opens at a temperature of somewhere between 40 and 90 degrees F, depending on the design of your fridge. Most are between 50 and 70. It does not close again until well below 32. Ice is cold enough to keep it closed, but not to close it again if it opens. Therefore, when you are diagnosing a defrost problem, it's a good idea to try to avoid melting the ice encasing the terminating thermostat until you've made your diagnosis. If the thermostat opens before you've had a chance to see if the heater works, you'll have to by-pass it. On some models, this involves cutting, stripping and splicing wires. No big deal, but it's an extra step

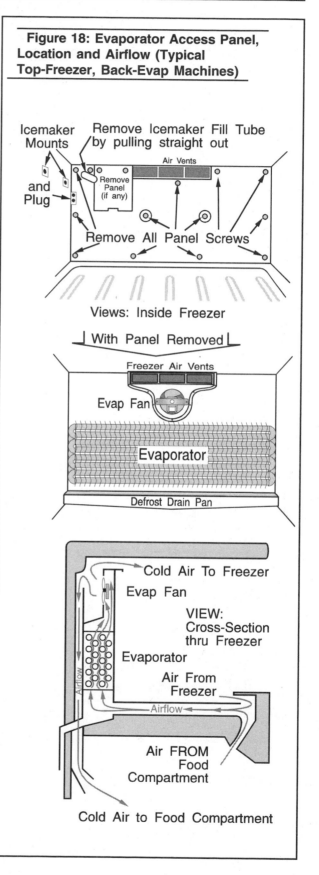

Figure 18: Evaporator Access Panel, Location and Airflow (Typical Top-Freezer, Back-Evap Machines)

Figure 19: Evaporator Access Panel, Location, and Airflow (Typical Top-Freezer, Bottom-Evap Machines

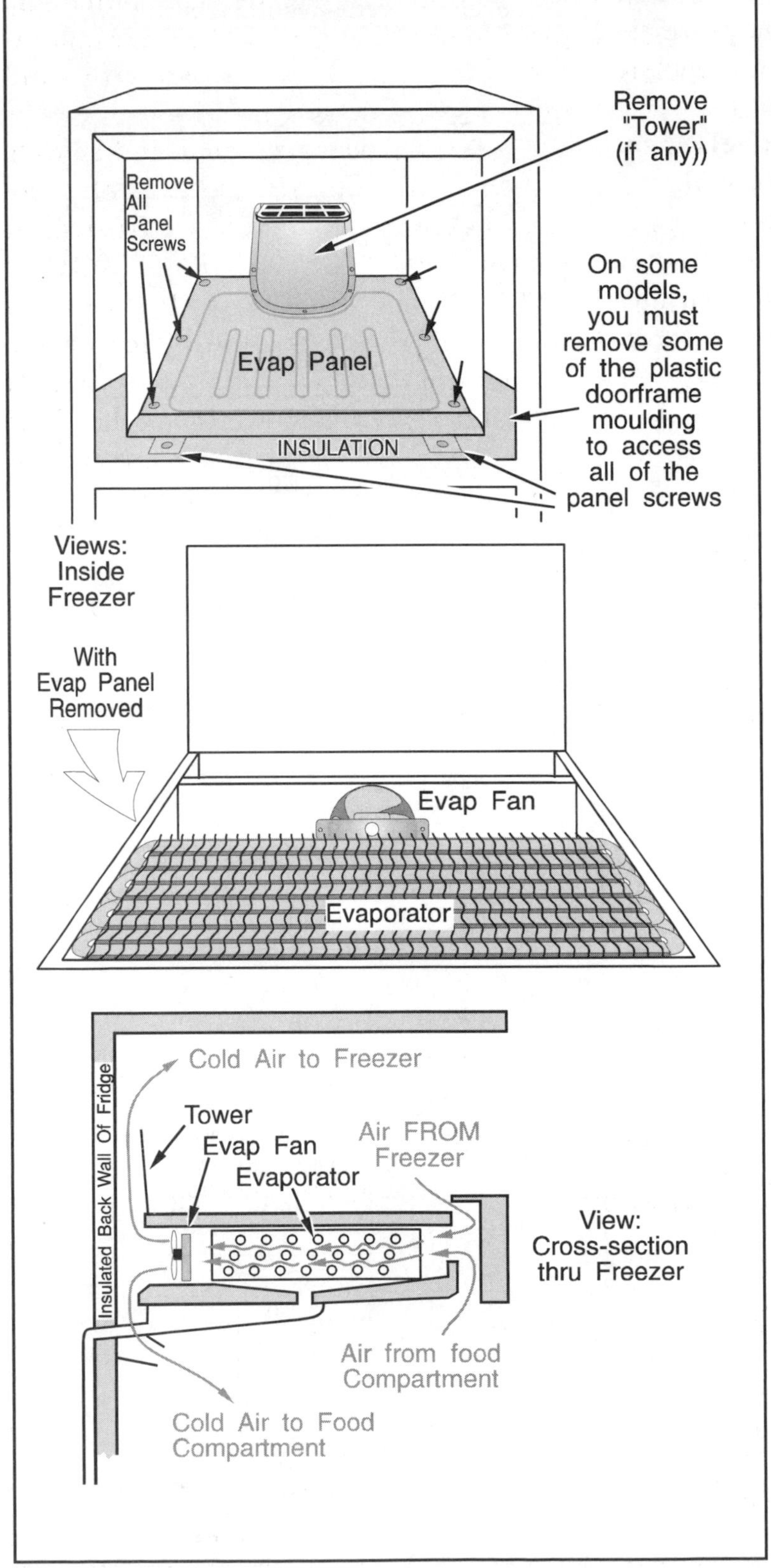

Remove "Tower" (if any))

Remove All Panel Screws

Evap Panel

INSULATION

On some models, you must remove some of the plastic doorframe moulding to access all of the panel screws

Views: Inside Freezer

With Evap Panel Removed

Evap Fan

Evaporator

Insulated Back Wall Of Fridge

Cold Air to Freezer

Tower
Evap Fan
Evaporator

Air FROM Freezer

View: Cross-section thru Freezer

Air from food Compartment

Cold Air to Food Compartment

that's unnecessary if you're careful about melting ice in the first place.

Some of the styrofoam insulation panels may be waterlogged and may break when you remove them. It's okay, just keep them in one piece as much as possible and replace them as best you can when you're re-assembling.

EVAPORATOR TYPES

There are countless different arrangements for the evaporator and its fan and ducting, but almost all arrangements are relatively simple and easy to trace.

The evaporator looks like a group of looped aluminum tubes, usually with fins attached. The fins are sharp; be careful not to cut your hands on them.

Chill-plate evaporators look like a silver aluminum plate, sometimes in the form of a box. There are many styles, but most are variations of the three types pictured in Figure 20.

A *back-evaporator* model is one with the evaporator mounted vertically against the *inside back wall* of the freezer compartment. These may be bottom freezer models, side-by-sides (Figure 17) or top freezer models (Figure 18.)

A *bottom-evaporator* model is one with the evaporator mounted horizontally (flat) beneath a panel on the *bottom* of the freezer compartment (Figure 19). These are generally top-freezer models only.

WHEN YOU GET THE PANEL OFF, examine the *quality* of the ice that's built up on the evaporator. Is it frosted heavily enough to block the airflow, or is it just a thin white coating? Does it have a fluffy (snowy) white consistency, or is it solid and clear-ish or slightly milky white-ish?

Check the frost *pattern*. Is the evaporator frosted on one or two coils, and then clear on the rest? Or is it pretty evenly frosted? Or is it not frosted at all?

On back-evap models, examine the drain pan directly beneath the evaporator. Is it clear, or is it filled with solid ice?

Each of these symptoms indicates a different problem. If you have solid ice, see Chapter 6. If no coils are frosted, or just one or two, see "UNEVEN FROST PATTERNS," section 4-8. If you see a thin, even, white coating of ice on the evaporator, and no ice in the defrost drain pan, the defrost system is probably O.K.; go to section 4-9. If you have lots of white, snowy ice, keep reading.

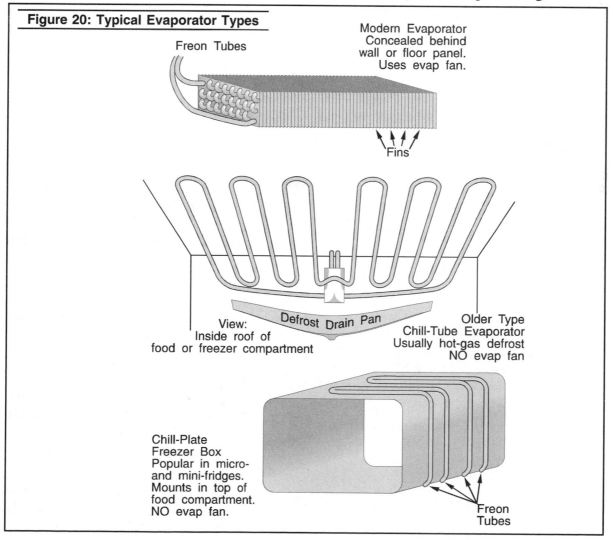

Figure 20: Typical Evaporator Types

Freon Tubes

Modern Evaporator Concealed behind wall or floor panel. Uses evap fan.

Fins

Defrost Drain Pan

View: Inside roof of food or freezer compartment

Older Type Chill-Tube Evaporator Usually hot-gas defrost NO evap fan

Chill-Plate Freezer Box Popular in micro- and mini-fridges. Mounts in top of food compartment. NO evap fan.

Freon Tubes

4-5 DEFROST SYSTEM

If the frost is snowy and white in appearance, you have a defrost problem. The three main components of the defrost system are the defrost timer, the defrost heater and the terminating thermostat.

4-5(a) DEFROST TIMERS AND ADAPTIVE DEFROST CONTROL

In most older refrigerators and some newer ones, a motor-driven timer (Figure 21) is used to stop the compressor and initiate a defrost cycle. This timer controls how often the cycle occurs, and how long the defrost heater stays on. This is a fixed cycle; for example, the refrigerator might stay in the cooling cycle for 10 hours, then spend 20 minutes in the defrost cycle.

There is one type of older refrigerator that uses a different kind of motorized timer. If you have a Whirlpool or Kenmore refrigerator with a flex-tray icemaker, the defrost timer is integrated into the icemaker. It is NOT a separate unit, like those shown in Figure 21. This is true whether you are using the icemaker to make ice or not; it is running constantly to time your defrost cycles. If you have a defrost problem and you have one of these machines, follow the instructions in section 4-6.

Nowadays, refrigerators are being made as efficient as possible, due in no small part to government energy efficiency requirements. Defrost heaters use a lot of energy, so designers are mimimizing the total amount of time that the heater is energized. The trick is in achieving a balance; that is, keeping the evaporator as clear of frost as necessary for efficient heat transfer, while energizing the heater as little as possible.

In practical terms, this translates to trying to reduce the **duration** of the defrost cycle (the length of time that the heater stays on) and to lengthen the defrost **interval** (the length of time between defrost cycles.)

Obviously, refrigerators operate under a wide variety of conditions, all of which affect the amount and speed of frost buildup. Such factors include ambient humidity and temperature, the water content and temperature of the food you put into the fridge, icemaking within the freezer, and how often the door is opened and closed.

For example, if you go away on vacation for a week, the refrigerator door will obviously not be opened for a long time. Less humid air will enter the fridge than if someone was at home, and opening and closing the door. Frost buildup will be much slower than usual, so the refrigerator will not need to be defrosted as often as normal. It also will not need to be chilled as often, so compressor run times will be shorter and less frequent.

Designers are using microprocessors (on solid state circuit boards) to adapt defrost intervals and durations to compensate for differences and changes in operating conditions. Such techniques are called **Adaptive Defrost Control**, commonly abbreviated as ADC.

To make decisions about the correct defrost duration and interval, the control board must have input about the conditions that the fridge is operating under. Each manufacturer uses a different logic scheme and different inputs, such as door open time, compressor run time, duration of the previous defrost cycle, and duration and intervals of door openings.

Door open info is provided to the logic board by the door switch - the same one that controls the refrigerator's internal lights. If the light bulb is not working, the ADC will still accumulate door open time. However, if the door switch has failed, the next defrost will occur either too quickly or too slowly.

Some designs even have a vacation mode; for example, the refrigerator will not defrost as often if the door has not been opened in 72 hours.

Some ADC / control boards control other functions of the refrigerator, too, such as icemaking and electrical air damper door opening and closing.

The defrost frequency may also be shortened under certain circumstances. For example, the ADC is programmed with a maximum amount of time that the heater can stay on; say, for 16 minutes. If the heater stays on for the maximum amount of time, without being terminated by the thermostat, the microprocessor will assume that not all of the frost melted, and it will initiate the next defrost cycle much sooner.

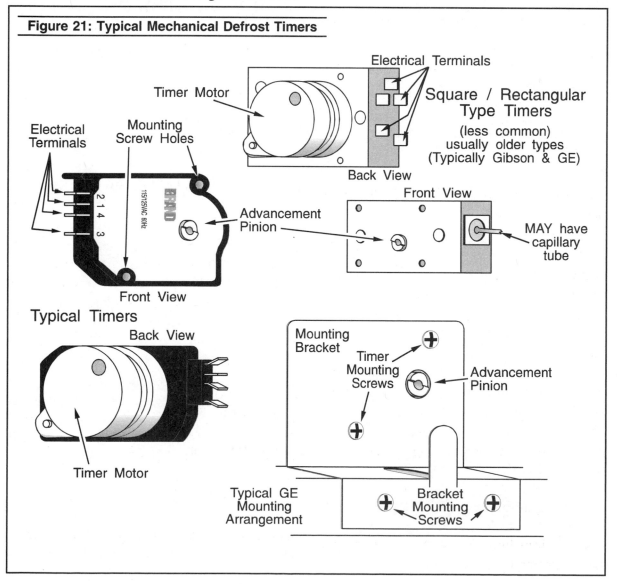

Figure 21: Typical Mechanical Defrost Timers

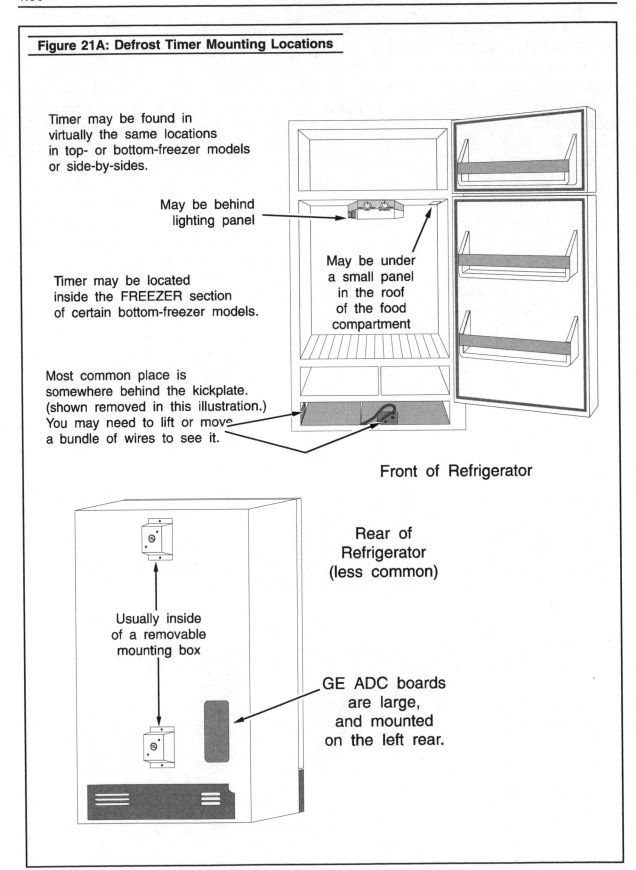

Figure 21A: Defrost Timer Mounting Locations

Timer may be found in
virtually the same locations
in top- or bottom-freezer models
or side-by-sides.

May be behind
lighting panel

May be under
a small panel
in the roof
of the food
compartment

Timer may be located
inside the FREEZER section
of certain bottom-freezer models.

Most common place is
somewhere behind the kickplate.
(shown removed in this illustration.)
You may need to lift or move
a bundle of wires to see it.

Front of Refrigerator

Rear of
Refrigerator
(less common)

Usually inside
of a removable
mounting box

GE ADC boards
are large,
and mounted
on the left rear.

DEFROST TIMER AND ADC BOARD LOCATIONS

Mechanical defrost timers can be a bit difficult to find. They come in many different styles. Often they are mounted under a cover plate or in a bracket that hides all but the advancement pinion. Figure 21 shows some different style timers and what the timer might look like installed; Figure 21A shows some typical mounting locations.

ADC boards are mounted in similar locations to defrost timers. However, they do not look the same as a mechanical timer. Being a solid-state circuit board, they do not have an advancement pinion; defrost is initiated differently than with timers (See section 4-5(d).) Figure 21B shows a typical ADC board. The easiest way to recognize them is that the harness connection is always labelled with the compressor, defrost heater, L1 and L2. Often the leads are labelled for the defrost thermostat, too, and a sometimes even test connections.

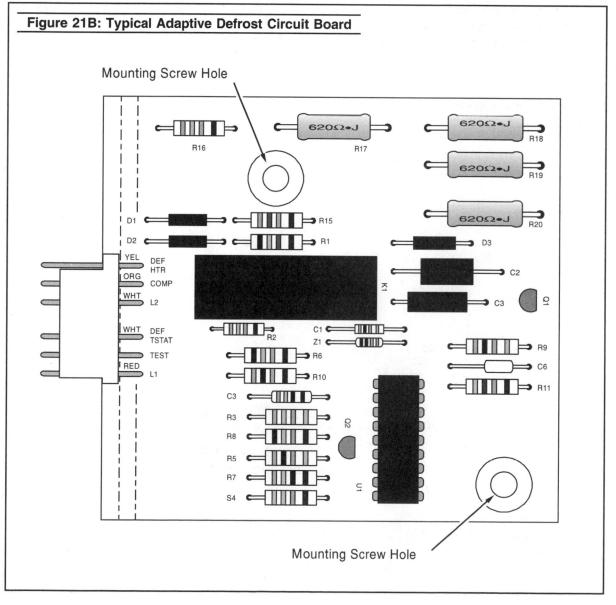

Figure 21B: Typical Adaptive Defrost Circuit Board

4-5(b) DEFROST HEATER

Defrost heaters are always located in the evaporator compartment. See Figures 22A, 22B, 22C & 22D for arrangement and types. There are three different types most commonly used:

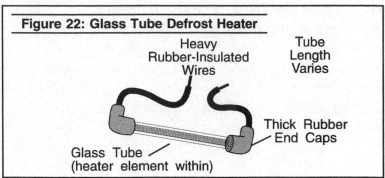

Figure 22: Glass Tube Defrost Heater

Heavy Rubber-Insulated Wires

Tube Length Varies

Thick Rubber End Caps

Glass Tube (heater element within)

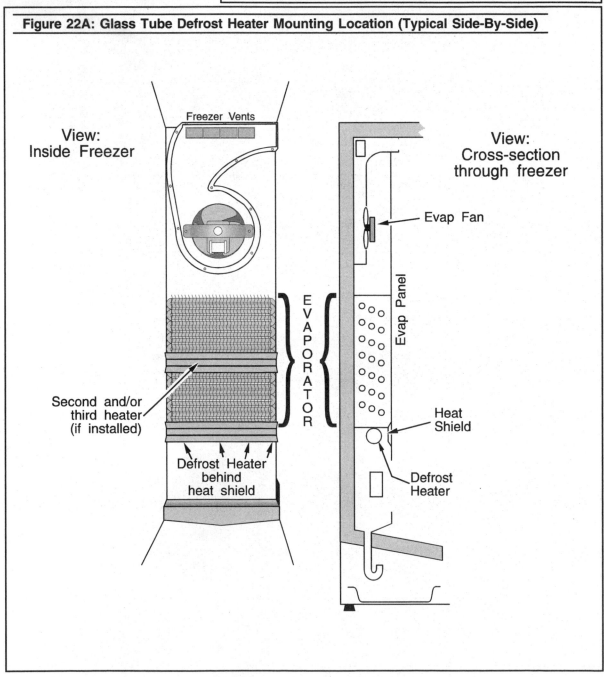

Figure 22A: Glass Tube Defrost Heater Mounting Location (Typical Side-By-Side)

Freezer Vents

View: Inside Freezer

EVAPORATOR

Second and/or third heater (if installed)

Defrost Heater behind heat shield

View: Cross-section through freezer

Evap Fan

Evap Panel

Heat Shield

Defrost Heater

22, 22A, 22B) Glass-tube defrost heaters: The heating element is encased in a glass tube mounted beneath the evaporator. Sometimes two or three small glass-tube-type heaters will be used instead of one big one; usually you'll see this arrangement in side-by-sides.

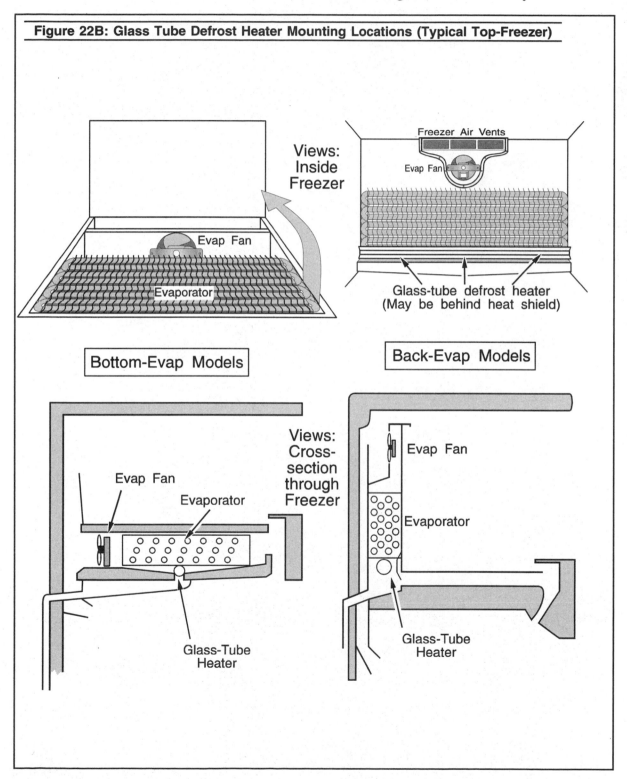

Figure 22B: Glass Tube Defrost Heater Mounting Locations (Typical Top-Freezer)

Views: Inside Freezer

Freezer Air Vents

Evap Fan

Evap Fan

Evaporator

Glass-tube defrost heater (May be behind heat shield)

Bottom-Evap Models

Back-Evap Models

Views: Cross-section through Freezer

Evap Fan

Evaporator

Evap Fan

Evaporator

Glass-Tube Heater

Glass-Tube Heater

22C) Aluminum tube heaters: These heaters look just like the evaporator tubes and press into the evaporator fins. They are usually used on bottom-evap models. The easiest way to see the heater is to look for the heavy, rubber-coated wires leading to it; one on each end. Often there are clips holding the ends on to the evaporator coils; watch for these when you remove the heater.

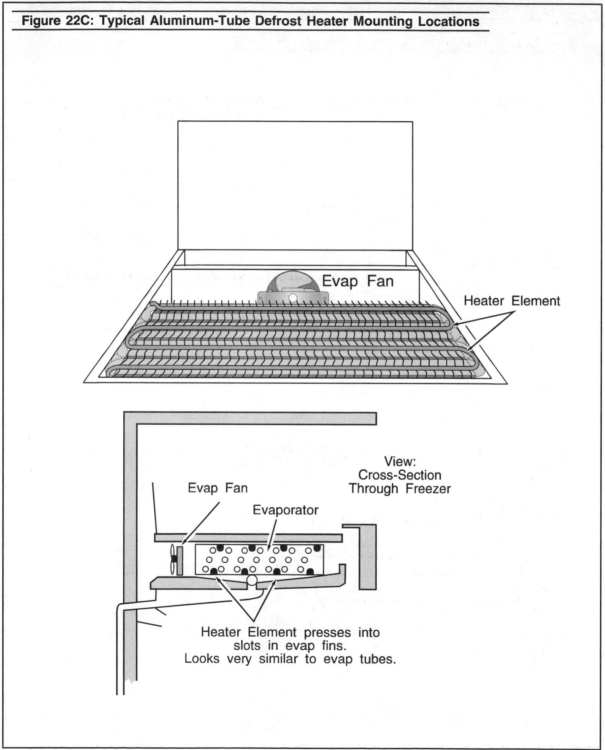

Figure 22C: Typical Aluminum-Tube Defrost Heater Mounting Locations

Evap Fan

Heater Element

View:
Cross-Section
Through Freezer

Evap Fan

Evaporator

Heater Element presses into
slots in evap fins.
Looks very similar to evap tubes.

22D) Bare element heaters: Found most commonly on top-freezer back-evap models. The element has no protective tubing and generally wraps around beneath the evaporator in a large "U" shape.

You must exercise caution when handling these heaters to prevent burning yourself. They all run very hot; glass tube and bare element heaters even glow red while in operation.

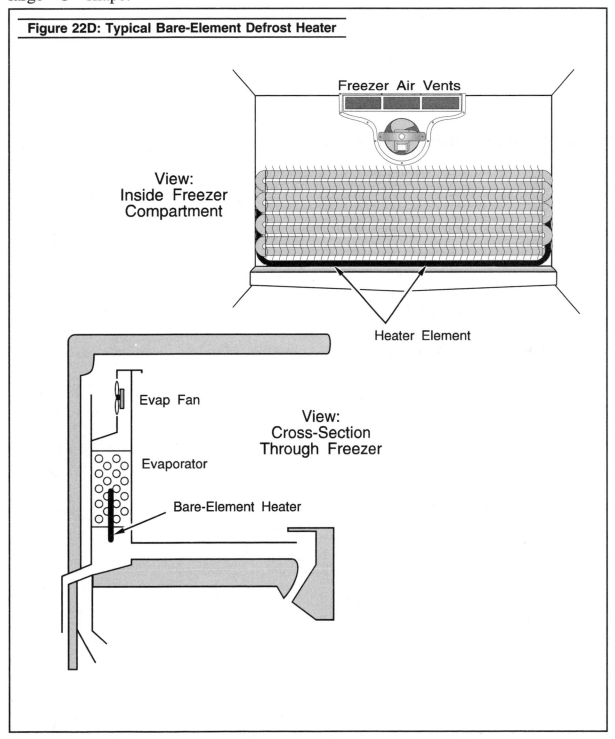

Figure 22D: Typical Bare-Element Defrost Heater

Freezer Air Vents

View: Inside Freezer Compartment

Heater Element

Evap Fan

View: Cross-Section Through Freezer

Evaporator

Bare-Element Heater

4-5(c) TERMINATING THERMOSTAT

A terminating thermostat will also be located somewhere in the evaporator compartment, usually to the evaporator itself (by a spring clip) or against the side or back wall of the compartment. It looks like a small cylindrical disc about 1" or so in diameter and about 3/4" to 1" thick (Figure 23.)

It is wired in series with the defrost heater; when it opens, the heater shuts off. One of the two heater wires will lead directly to it.

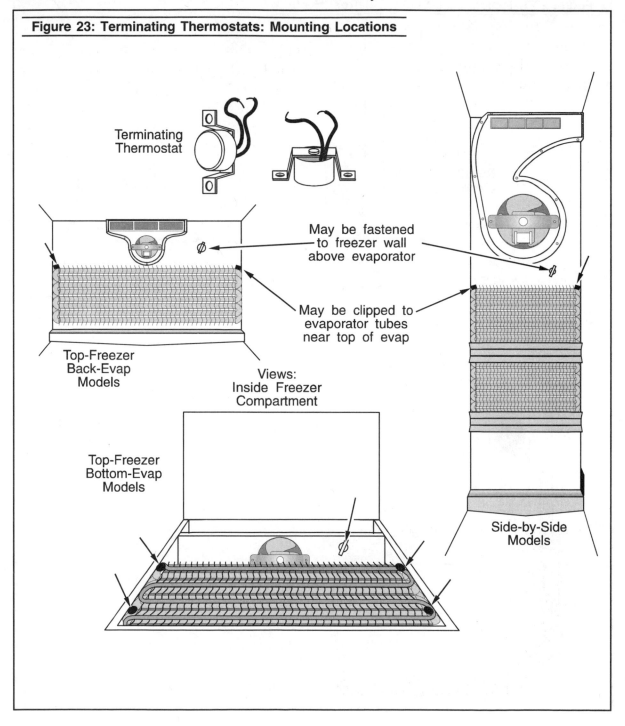

Figure 23: Terminating Thermostats: Mounting Locations

Terminating Thermostat

May be fastened to freezer wall above evaporator

May be clipped to evaporator tubes near top of evap

Top-Freezer Back-Evap Models

Views: Inside Freezer Compartment

Top-Freezer Bottom-Evap Models

Side-by-Side Models

4-5(d). DEFROST SYSTEM DIAGNOSIS AND REPAIR

Defrost *starts* when a timer turns on the defrost heater. The timer may be mechanical and motor driven, or it may be an electronic ADC board.

Defrost *stops* when one of two things happens.

If the evaporator is lightly frosted, the frost will melt fairly quickly. If that happens, you want to turn the heater off soon after the ice melts, to prevent the evaporator compartment from heating up too much. If the **terminating thermostat** senses too high a temperature in the compartment, it opens, and cuts power to the heater. The thermostat will then stay open until the compartment again reaches a very low temperature. In other words, it waits to reset itself until the cooling cycle starts again.

If the evaporator is more heavily frosted, the ice may not all melt within the time allotted by the timer. In this case, the terminating thermostat will remain closed throughout the defrost cycle. The heater will stay on until the *timer* stops the defrost cycle, and restarts the cooling cycle.

If you initiate defrost (turn the timer on) and the heater *does not* heat up, then usually the heater or terminating thermostat is bad. If you initiate defrost and the heater *does* turn on, then usually the timer or ADC board is bad, and you must replace it.

To diagnose which component is bad, you must initiate the defrost mode, or test continuity through the defrost heater and terminating thermostat. How you initiate defrost depends on whether you have a mechanical defrost timer or an ADC board.

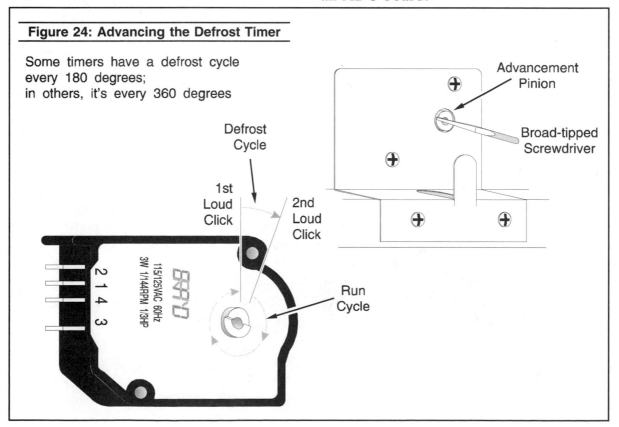

Figure 24: Advancing the Defrost Timer

Some timers have a defrost cycle every 180 degrees; in others, it's every 360 degrees

Defrost Cycle

1st Loud Click

2nd Loud Click

Run Cycle

Advancement Pinion

Broad-tipped Screwdriver

115/125VAC 60Hz
3W 1/144RPM 1/3HP

INITIATING DEFROST: MECHANICAL TIMER

If you have a mechanical defrost timer, find the timer (see section 4-5(a).) Put a screwdriver in the advancement pinion and advance it (clockwise *only*, or you will break it). (Figure 24) Sometimes it takes a pretty firm twist to advance it. You will feel it clicking. At some spot in the cycle, you will hear and feel a loud click; after you advance it 10-20 more degrees or so, you will feel and hear another loud click.

Between the two loud clicks is the defrost part of the cycle. The rest of the timer's rotation is the "run" cycle. If your compressor is running when you advance the defrost timer, it will stop running when you hit the defrost portion of the cycle.

Advance the timer all the way around to the beginning of the defrost cycle again (generally one-half or one full turn) and leave it as early in the defrost cycle as possible.

Now skip ahead to DEFROST HEATER DIAGNOSIS. If you have a hot-gas defroster, go now to section 4-7.

INITIATING DEFROST - ADC

If your fridge has Adaptive Defrost Controls, how you initiate defrost depends on the brand. See Appendix A in the back of this manual for instructions.

DEFROST HEATER DIAGNOSIS

Look and listen to the evaporator. Within ten minutes (usually much less) you should be able to see a red glow from the defrost heater(s), which is (are) mounted beneath the evaporator. If you have an aluminum-tube heater as described in section 4-5(b), it will not glow

red, but you *will* see ice melting away from its coils. Be careful; all defrost heaters run hot enough to burn you. You will probably also hear popping and sizzling; this is defrost water hitting the heater and boiling off.

If you *do* see or hear any of these indications, the problem is the defrost timer or ADC board; it is not initiating defrost. Timers can get old, worn and coked up with dust, and may develop hard spots in the bearings. If you *do not* hear or see indications that the defrost heater is working, then it is necessary to investigate a little further. Go to Section 4-5(e).

REPLACING THE DEFROST TIMER

If the problem is your timer, it must be replaced.

If the timer is connected by a terminal block, it probably plugs in directly.

If you have separate wires to the timer terminals, carefully record which wire came off which terminal, by color or by terminal number, or both. Draw a picture, if you have to. Make sure that the new timer is wired correctly; there should be instructions with the new timer.

CAUTION: If you have a Whirlpool or Kenmore timer with a separate wire coming from the timer motor, (Figure 25) it is important to get that wire connected to the proper terminal. If the wire is visible on the old timer, connect it to the same terminal. If you cannot tell for sure, get the information for your model fridge from your parts man. If the timer is wired incorrectly, the fridge will frost up again.

Thoroughly melt all the ice in the evaporator compartment and in the air ducts leading to and from the compartment, and re-assemble your fridge.

4-5(e). DIAGNOSIS: DEFROST HEATER AND TERMINATING THERMOSTAT

If you do not hear or see indications that the defrost heater is working, you could be looking at one of several different problems. The heater element *may* be burnt. The heater *may* be so icebound that it would take *hours* for the heater to melt enough ice for you to see the heater begin to work. The terminating thermostat might be open.

Whether you have an ammeter or not, if you think the defrost heater is not working, test it for continuity.

If you don't have an ammeter, thoroughly melt all the ice in the evaporator compartment and find the proper power leads for your heater. If they are not connected to a terminal block, you will need to cut the leads to test for continuity. Make sure you're not testing continuity across the terminating thermostat too; it may be wide open above 40 or 50 degrees. If the heater shows good continuity, it is working fine. If you have more than one heater, test each, unless they are permanently wired in series. If they are permanently wired in series, test them as a set. If the heater is bad, replace it. If you have multiple heaters, replace them as a set. With glass-tube heaters, be careful that the glass is not cracked or broken and that you do not cut yourself. It is a good idea to replace the terminating thermostat with the heater(s). It's cheap.

If you have an ammeter, try to determine if the heater is drawing any power before you melt any ice. If so, it will be drawing between about **2** and **5** amps. In trying to find the heater leads, be careful that you do not melt so much ice that the terminating thermostat opens. If you suspect that the terminating thermostat might be open, temporarily bypass the terminating thermostat with an alligator jumper as described below.

If you cannot find the heater leads, an alterna-

Figure 25: Whirlpool / Kenmore Defrost Timer Motor Wire

Loose wire goes either on terminal 1 or terminal 2. To determine which:

1) Check the old timer
2) Check a wiring diagram
3) Ask your parts dealer

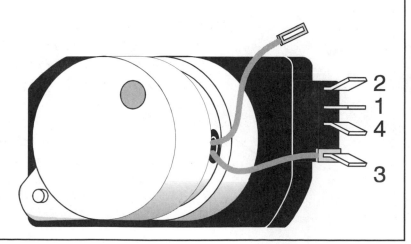

tive is to check the current in one lead of the main power cord. (See Figure 7) If the fridge is in the defrost cycle and the interior lights are off, then the only current draw will be the defrost heater.

If the heater(s) test out O.K., then the problem is your terminating thermostat. Double-check this diagnosis by jumping across (shorting) the terminating thermostat with your alligator jumpers. If the two thermostat leads are not on a terminal block, you will have to cut the leads to jump the thermostat. Start the defrost system as described earlier in this section. If the defrost heater now heats up, your terminating thermostat is definitely bad. Replace it.

In replacing heaters and/or terminating thermostats, you can use butt connectors, wirenuts, and electrical tape, or spade connectors if fitted. Remember that it's a wet environment.

LIFTING THE EVAPORATOR

If you have a bottom-evap model fridge, replacing the heater will involve the delicate task of lifting the evaporator up to get to the heater. (See Figure 26)

The Freon tubes leading to the evaporator will both enter the evaporator at one end. If you break or puncture one of those tubes, you're looking at a potentially expensive sealed system repair.

Thaw out the evaporator as thoroughly as is humanly possible. The closer the tubes are to room temperature, the more malleable the metal will be. Do not heat the tubes. If you are changing an aluminum-tube defrost heater, remove any clips holding it to the

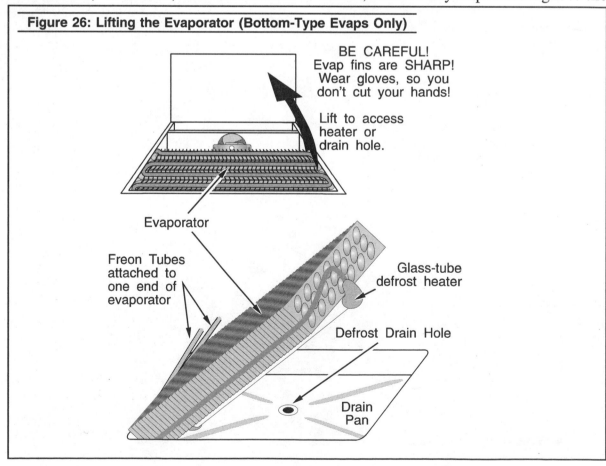

Figure 26: Lifting the Evaporator (Bottom-Type Evaps Only)

BE CAREFUL!
Evap fins are SHARP!
Wear gloves, so you don't cut your hands!

Lift to access heater or drain hole.

Evaporator

Freon Tubes attached to one end of evaporator

Glass-tube defrost heater

Defrost Drain Hole

Drain Pan

evaporator and loosen the top heater coils from the evaporator fins. The evaporator fins are sharp; be careful you don't cut yourself. Remove the evaporator mounting screws (if there *are* any) and gently lift up the end of the evaporator opposite the tubes. Prop up the evaporator with a blunt instrument (I use my electrical pliers or a flashlight) and change the heater. While you're in there, make sure the drain is clear as described in Chapter 6. Do what you went in there to do, but as much as possible, avoid moving the evaporator around *too* much.

When you finish, gently lower the evaporator back into place. Always re-install any little chunks of styrofoam or duck seal that you may have removed from *beside* the evaporator; they keep the air flowing *through* the evaporator rather than *around* it.

Re-assemble the fridge.

4-6. WHIRLPOOL/KENMORE FLEX-TRAY ICEMAKER DEFROST SYSTEM

You can recognize this type of defrost system by the shape of the cube it puts out (or *would* put out, if it was working). The hard-tray Whirlpool/ Kenmore produces "half-moon" shaped cubes (see Figure 27.) The flex-tray produces "rounded rectangular" cubes. The hard tray is finished in a dark gray or black color and has rotating fingers that eject the cubes from the unit; the flex-tray has a white plastic, flexible tray that inverts and twists to eject, much the same as a manual ice cube tray would work. The hard-tray and separate defrost timer is by far the more common arrangement.

This defrost system has the same components described in the defrost system in section 4-5, except that the defrost timer is integrated into the icemaker. Whether it is being used to make ice or not, the icemaker motor runs whenever the compressor is running.

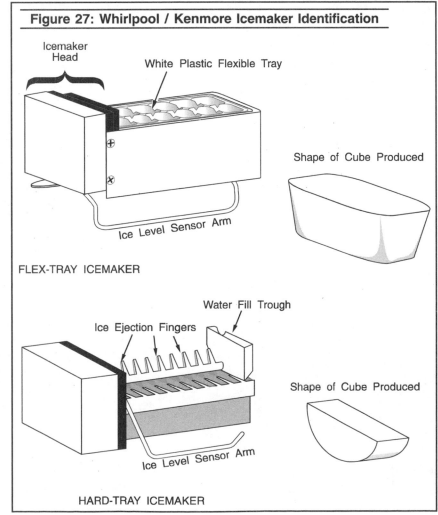

Figure 27: Whirlpool / Kenmore Icemaker Identification

Icemaker Head

White Plastic Flexible Tray

Shape of Cube Produced

Ice Level Sensor Arm

FLEX-TRAY ICEMAKER

Water Fill Trough

Ice Ejection Fingers

Shape of Cube Produced

Ice Level Sensor Arm

HARD-TRAY ICEMAKER

The defrost components will act the same, and you test them in the same manner as described in section 4-5, except for one item:

You cannot advance the icemaker like you can advance a defrost timer. However, the actual switch that controls the heater *is* accessible.

Remove the icemaker and the evaporator panel as described in section 4-4. *YOUR COMPRESSOR WILL STOP RUNNING WHEN YOU UNPLUG YOUR ICEMAKER. DO NOT BE ALARMED.* Remove the ice tray from the icemaker. It is spring loaded and simply pushes away from the icemaker head and pops out. Take the plastic cover off the face of the icemaker and remove the three screws holding the metal faceplate to the icemaker head. (See Figure 28) Remove the drive cam, the large drive gear and the smaller timing gear. You will need to remove the leaf switch to get the drive cam off. Examine the gears for any stripped teeth. If you see any, replace the gears and drive pin as a set.

Temporarily remount the leaf switch to keep it from drifting around and touching things.

Inside your fridge, turn the cold control to its coldest setting. Plug the icemaker back into its electrical socket and observe the drive motor in the upper lefthand corner of the icemaker head. When the compressor is running, the motor will turn very slowly. If it doesn't, it is bad. Replace it.

Unplug your icemaker and look into the icemaker head. The defrost switch is the small, rectangular switch in the upper

righthand corner of the icemaker head. Remove this switch from its mounts, but do not disconnect the wires to it. Using electrical tape, tape it out of the way so it does not touch any other metal object in the icemaker head. Plug in the icemaker again. *Do not touch any metal contact with your hands; you may shock yourself.*

Within a few minutes, you should start to see signs that the defrost heater is working as described in section 4-5(d).

IF YOU SEE OR HEAR NO SIGNS OF THE DEFROST HEATER HEATING UP, unplug your icemaker, remove the BLACK lead from the defrost switch and electrically test the switch for opening and closing. Using your resistance meter, you should see continuity (and no resistance) between the empty terminal (where the BLACK lead *was*) and the

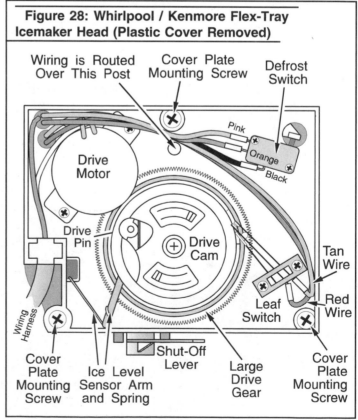

Figure 28: Whirlpool / Kenmore Flex-Tray Icemaker Head (Plastic Cover Removed)

PINK terminal. You should see NO continuity between the empty (BLACK) and ORANGE terminal. When the switch toggle is depressed, continuity will be just the opposite: BLACK-ORANGE-CONTINUITY, BLACK-PINK-NO CONTINUITY. If the switch is not acting right, replace it. If the switch is okay, the problem is probably your defrost heater or terminating thermostat. Diagnose and repair as described in section 4-5(e).

IF YOUR DEFROST HEATER <u>DID</u> HEAT UP when you dismounted the defrost switch, then you need to replace the gear sets in your icemaker. Get *both* sets of gears (timing gears *and* drive gears) from your appliance parts dealer. Alignment of the gears is critical; follow the instructions that come with the gear sets carefully. When you replace the gear sets, it is also a good idea to replace the defrost switch. You may or may not want to replace the drive motor. They *do* quit on occasion, but they *are* a bit more expensive. If you replace the motor, you will have to re-align the defrost timing gear mechanism.

RE-ASSEMBLY

If you have not removed the defrost timing gear housing from the back of the icemaker head or the motor from the front of the head, you will not need to re-align the *defrost timing* gear mechanism. However, you *will* need to realign the *drive* gear mechanism.

Align the hole in the small drive gear with the alignment hole in the icemaker head and install the gear. Check alignment by inserting a 3/32" rod (a drill bit will do) into the holes to make sure they line up. See Figure 29. If they do not line up perfectly, momentarily plug the icemaker in or apply 110 volt power to the two center leads of the plug This will turn the drive motor slightly. Repeat the process until the holes align.

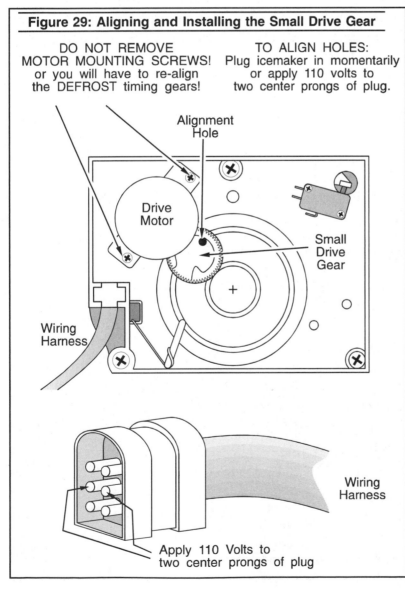

Figure 29: Aligning and Installing the Small Drive Gear

DO NOT REMOVE MOTOR MOUNTING SCREWS! or you will have to re-align the DEFROST timing gears!

TO ALIGN HOLES: Plug icemaker in momentarily or apply 110 volts to two center prongs of plug.

Alignment Hole

Drive Motor

Small Drive Gear

Wiring Harness

Wiring Harness

Apply 110 Volts to two center prongs of plug

Install the large drive gear and align it on the same alignment hole. A second alignment hole is shown in Figure 30. The large drive gear must line up on *both* alignment holes *and* on the large drive cam hole in the center of the icemaker head.

Carefully holding the drive gear in its aligned position, install the drive cam (Figure 31.) Make sure the spring-loaded drive pin is in place in the cam and retained properly; the cam's spring-retainer should be in the pin's groove. Line the drive pin up on its hole on the drive gear. Lift the spring-loaded shut-off arm (ice level sensor) as you install the cam and let it rest in the cam hollow. Be sure that the ice level sensor arm loading spring is in the right place. Install the leaf switch. Sometimes the stuff in this paragraph takes three hands and

your belly, but be persistent. You'll get it together.

Make sure the wiring for the leaf switch and the defrost switch is routed *over* the post above the drive gear. Carefully install the metal cover plate, making sure the end of the wire shut-off arm (ice level sensor) is in its pivot hole in the metal cover plate. Install your three screws. The drive pin will pop up through the metal cover plate.

Install the ice tray into the ice maker, and re-assemble your fridge.

The icemaker is now aligned at the beginning of an ejection cycle. When you re-install it, the ice tray will slowly turn 1 full turn. If the icemaker is being used, the tray will then fill with water. Make sure the icemaker is turned on (ice level sensor arm is down) or it won't make ice.

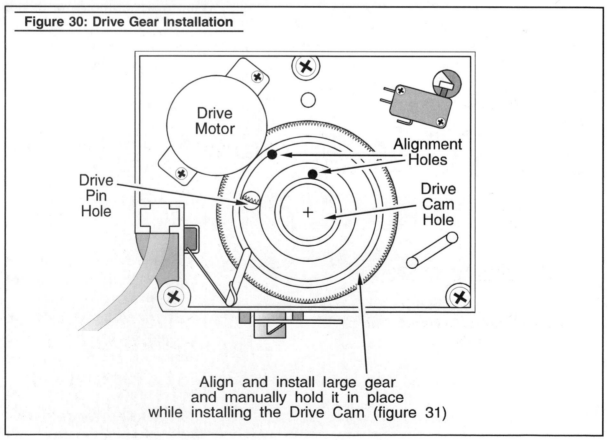

Figure 30: Drive Gear Installation

Align and install large gear
and manually hold it in place
while installing the Drive Cam (figure 31)

Figure 31: Installing the Drive Cam

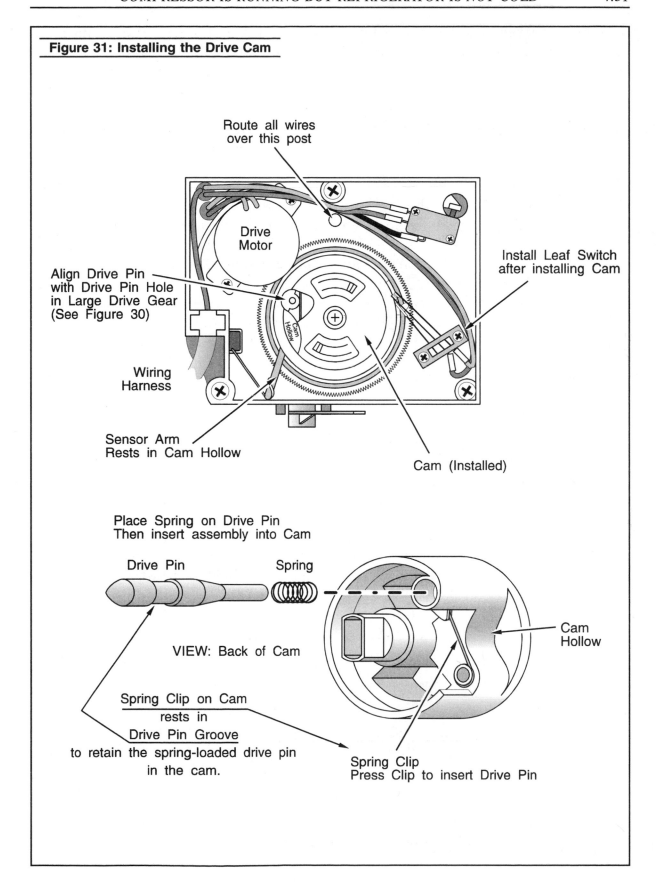

Route all wires over this post

Drive Motor

Align Drive Pin with Drive Pin Hole in Large Drive Gear (See Figure 30)

Install Leaf Switch after installing Cam

Cam Hollow

Wiring Harness

Sensor Arm Rests in Cam Hollow

Cam (Installed)

Place Spring on Drive Pin Then insert assembly into Cam

Drive Pin   Spring

Cam Hollow

VIEW: Back of Cam

Spring Clip on Cam
rests in
Drive Pin Groove
to retain the spring-loaded drive pin in the cam.

Spring Clip
Press Clip to insert Drive Pin

4-7 HOT GAS DEFROST PROBLEMS

If you have a refrigerator with a hot gas defrost system, the defrost mechanism is somewhat different from those described in previous sections of this book. If you suspect that you might have a hot-gas defroster but you are not sure, ask your appliance parts dealer. Most of these refrigerators were built before 1970, but not all.

The main difference in a hot gas system is that there is no electrical heater or separate terminating thermostat. The defrost cycle <u>is</u> controlled by a defrost timer similar to the one you'll find in electric defrost systems, but the timer controls a *solenoid valve* instead of a *heater*. When this valve opens, it diverts the hot Freon gas coming out of the compressor. It then will flow through the *evaporator* instead of the *condenser*. The hot Freon gas flowing through the evaporator melts the frost from it. In order to supply the hot Freon gas needed to melt the frost, the compressor keeps running throughout the defrost cycle.

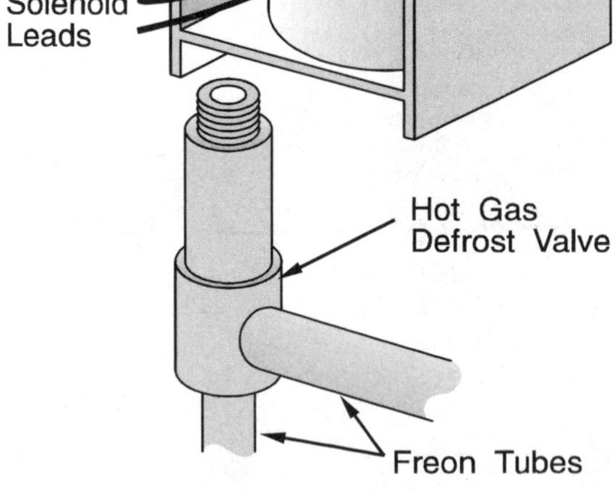

Another interesting feature of most of these refrigerators is that the defrost terminating thermostat was built into the defrost timer. These units have a temperature sensing bulb, similar to that found on the cold control (see section 4-9 and Figures 21 and 33) as a part of the timer. The sensing bulb is led to, and rests against, the evaporator. Its function is to sense the temperature of the evaporator so the defrost mechanism knows when to shut off.

Troubleshooting a defrost problem in this system involves two steps. First, find your defrost timer as described in section 4-5(a). Advance it into the defrost cycle as described in section 4-5(d). The compressor will *not* stop running. Wait and watch your evaporator for 10-15 minutes.

If the frost starts to melt, then your defrost timer has gone bad. Thoroughly melt the rest of the frost from your evaporator and replace the defrost timer.

If the frost does *not* start to melt, then your defrost solenoid is probably bad. Fortunately, the defrost solenoid is usually designed so the electrical coil can be replaced without cutting into the sealed system. You will find the coil behind the back bottom panel of the refrigerator. Trace the Freon tubing until you find electrical wires joining the tubing at a certain point. This will be the solenoid valve. (Figure 32). Replace the coil (solenoid) on the valve. Re-assemble your fridge.

Figure 32: Hot Gas Defrost Solenoid Valve

4-8. UNEVEN FROST PATTERNS, OR NO FROST AT ALL

The evaporator should be bitterly cold to the touch. In fact, when you touch it, your finger will often *stick* to it. If the evaporator is either slightly cool or not cold at all, and your compressor is running *constantly* (not short-cycling; see section 4-9) you have a more serious problem. The same diagnosis applies if just the first coil or two in the evaporator is (are) frosted and the rest are relatively free of ice or perhaps even lukewarm.

What's happening is that the Freon is not getting compressed enough in the compressor. This could be due to two causes: either the amount of Freon in the system is low, or the compressor is worn out. It's time to call a technician out to your home, if you feel your fridge is worth saving. It *may* only require recharging the Freon system, which, depending on the refrigerant used, may cost you a little, or a LOT. I have only seen one exception to this diagnosis, and this is described in section 7-2.

Don't let the age of the refrigerator affect your diagnosis. Not too long ago, one of the largest appliance companies put out a series of refrigerators with compressors that were either poorly designed or poorly constructed; I never did find out which. These were their giant, 20 to 25 cubic-foot flagship models, with techno-marvelous gadgets like digital self-diagnosis and ice and water in the door, and they were built with compressors that wore out within 2 years. For-

tunately, the biggest and best companies warrant their refrigerators for five years or more, so these refrigerators were still covered under warranty. In my opinion, there *is* a real advantage to buying brand-name appliances.

4-9. COLD CONTROL

If your refrigerator is cold but not as cold as usual, and you cannot trace it to any of the other problems in this chapter, your cold control may be defective. To test its cut-in and cut-out temperatures, you can *try* putting the capillary bulb in ice water and measuring the temperature with a thermometer, but it's a wet, messy, job and it's difficult to control the temperatures. It's easier to just try replacing it and see if the fridge starts acting properly.

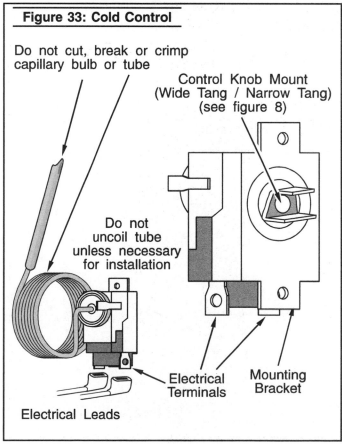

Figure 33: Cold Control

Do not cut, break or crimp capillary bulb or tube

Control Knob Mount (Wide Tang / Narrow Tang) (see figure 8)

Do not uncoil tube unless necessary for installation

Electrical Terminals

Mounting Bracket

Electrical Leads

If you hear your compressor "short-cycling" (starting and stopping at short intervals) try jumping across the two leads of the cold control with an alligator jumper. If there is a green *third* lead, ignore it for this test; it is the ground wire. If the fridge starts running constantly, the cold control is bad. Replace it.

To test or change the cold control, first find it as described in section 4-1. Pull the knob off it and remove any plastic cover plate or housing from it. (Figure 33)

You will see two wires leading to it. There will also be a thick, stiff **CAPILLARY TUBE** attached. The capillary tube is the liquid-filled temperature-sensing element of the cold control, and operates in the same manner as a ther-mometer bulb; in fact, the end of the capillary tube may have a bulb. The tube and bulb *may* be coiled right next to the cold control, or they *may* be led away to another part of the compartment.

If you are just *testing* (electrically) the cold control, you can jumper directly from one wire lead to the other. By doing this, you are closing the switch manually, and assuming the machine is not in the defrost mode, the compressor should start.

If you are *replacing* the cold control, it will be necessary to trace where the capillary tube goes, and remove the whole tube *with* the cold control. The new tube is replaced directly. Be careful not to kink the new tube (bend it too sharply) when installing it.

Chapter 5 Overview

Step-by-Step

Complaint: Warm refrigerator, or not as cold as usual
Chapter Qualifier: Compressor is not running

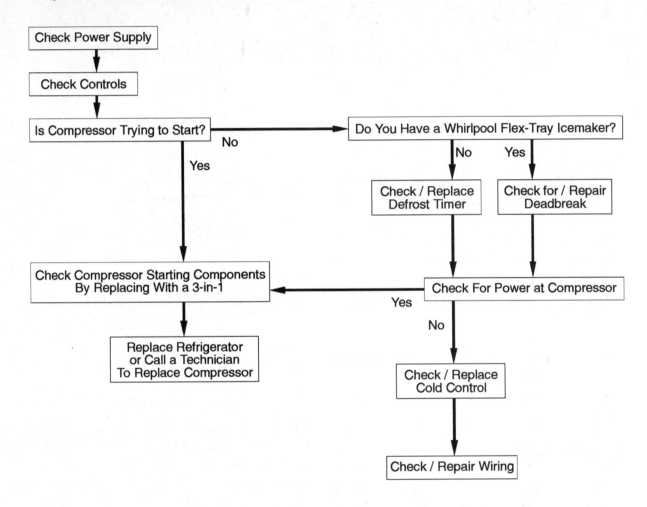

Chapter 5

REFRIGERATOR IS NOT COLD AND COMPRESSOR IS NOT RUNNING

5-1 POWER

If your refrigerator is not cold (or not as cold as usual) and you have determined that the compressor is *not* running (see the first page of Chapter 4,) first check that the fridge has power. If you have interior lights in the fridge, you have power. If you *don't* have interior lights, check your house breaker. Also check your wall outlet by unplugging the fridge and plugging in a portable appliance such as a blow-dryer or electric shaver.

5-2 CONTROLS

When you have established that power is getting to the fridge, check your controls. They sometimes have a way of getting magically turned off, especially in households with kids. (See section 4-1)

5-3. DIAGNOSIS AND REPAIR

Listen carefully to the fridge for a two or three minutes. If you hear a "CLICK-BUZZZZZ-CLICK" (with a buzz of between about 5 and 30 seconds) then you *are* getting power to the

compressor. There is something wrong with the compressor or compressor starting components (relay or overload.) See section 5-3(e).

5-3(a) DEFROST TIMER OR ADC BOARD

How you diagnose a non-starting compressor depends much upon whether you have a mechanical defrost timer or ADC (Adaptive Defrost Controls.)

If you have a fridge with ADC and the lights are on, and the compressor will not start, you need to check if you're getting voltage to the compressor starting components as described in Section 5-3(b). If you are not getting voltage to the starting components, the cold control or ADC board is bad. Check these components as described in section 5-3(c).

If you have a fridge with a mechanical timer and you hear nothing at all, set the cold control on the coldest setting and advance the defrost timer. If it is stuck in the defrost mode, the compressor will not run. The terminating thermostat will open and stop the heater at a certain temperature, so the fridge will *not* continue to heat up. You will hear, see and feel nothing but a fridge that's not cold. It's as if it wasn't even plugged in, except that the interior lights will still be on. (See section 4-5(d) and Figure 24 for details on how to advance the timer). Place a screwdriver in the advancement pinion and advance the timer manually (remember, clockwise *only*) about 1/4 to 3/8 of a turn. Does the compressor start? If it does, replace the defrost timer. If this does not start the compressor, make sure you leave the timer in the "run" mode for the rest of your diagnosis. Go to section 5-3(b).

In a Whirlpool flex-tray icemaker as described in section 4-6, the defrost timer is integrated into the icemaker. The defrost switch might fail into a "deadbreak" position in which nothing runs, similar to that described above. To test for deadbreak, first unplug and remove the icemaker from the freezer compartment. Look at the timing gear housing on the *back* of the icemaker head. You will see a white circle, about 5/8" in diameter (Figure 34). Examine the circle closely. You will see an arrow molded into the circle. If this arrow lines up with the arrow molded into the black timing gear housing, then you *might* have a deadbreak.

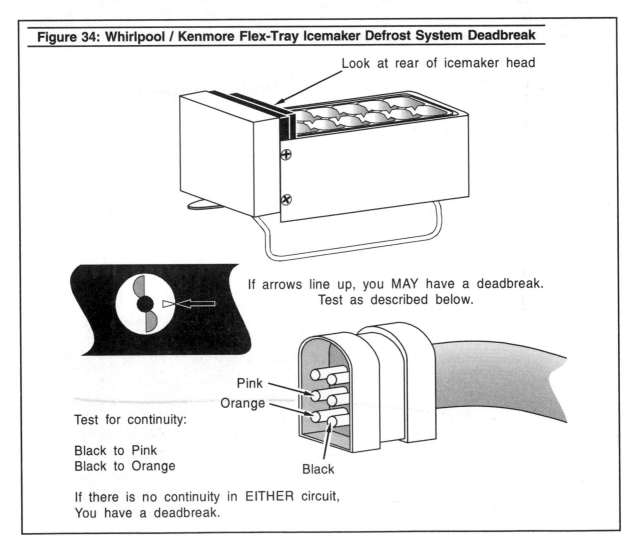

Figure 34: Whirlpool / Kenmore Flex-Tray Icemaker Defrost System Deadbreak

Look at rear of icemaker head

If arrows line up, you MAY have a deadbreak.
Test as described below.

Pink
Orange
Black

Test for continuity:

Black to Pink
Black to Orange

If there is no continuity in EITHER circuit,
You have a deadbreak.

Test for continuity between the BLACK and PINK terminals and the BLACK and ORANGE terminals of the plug (see Figure 34). One or the other should show continuity. If neither does, you have a deadbreak. Replace the defrost switch and gear sets as described in section 4-6.

5-3(b). TESTING THE COMPRESSOR FOR POWER

If you *still* hear nothing at all, pull off the lower back panel of the fridge, remove the compressor relay cover. This is the square-ish plastic or bakelite box attached to the side of the compressor.

Test for voltage at the two compressor leads. (Figure 35)

If you have voltage to the compressor but it is not starting, see section 5-3(e).

If you do not have voltage to the compressor, check the cold control as described in section 5-3(c).

5-3(c). COLD CONTROL

If you have a mechanical timer, and you don't have voltage to the compressor, use your alligator jumpers to connect the two wires of the cold control. (See section 4-9) If you now have power to the compressor, the cold control is bad. Replace it.

If you have ADC, jumper the cold control

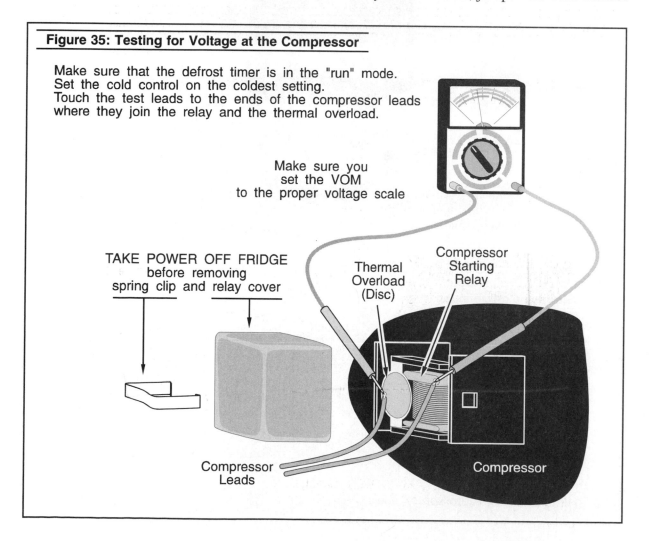

Figure 35: Testing for Voltage at the Compressor

Make sure that the defrost timer is in the "run" mode.
Set the cold control on the coldest setting.
Touch the test leads to the ends of the compressor leads where they join the relay and the thermal overload.

Make sure you set the VOM to the proper voltage scale

TAKE POWER OFF FRIDGE before removing spring clip and relay cover

Thermal Overload (Disc)

Compressor Starting Relay

Compressor Leads

Compressor

terminals as descibed above, and wait for 30 minutes, then check for voltage at the compressor. This will give the ADC time to finish any defrost cycle it might be in, and re-enter the cooling cycle. If you now have power to the compressor, the cold control is bad. Replace it. If not, the ADC board is bad. Replace it.

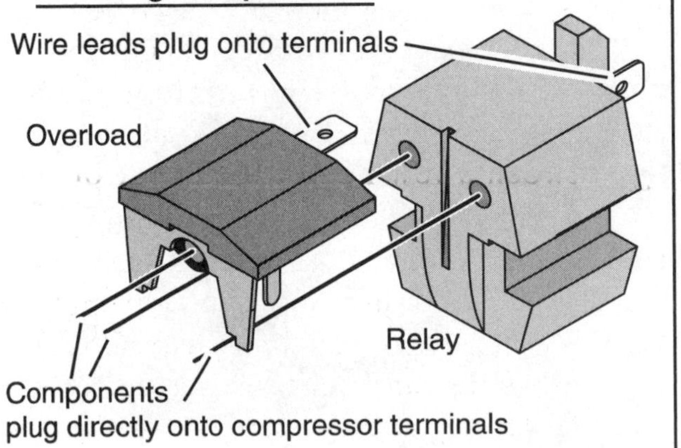

5-3(d). WIRING AND ELECTRICAL

If the test in section 5-3(c) doesn't start the compressor, you're going to have to get a wiring diagram (there *may* be one pasted to the back of the refrigerator) and start tracing wires with your VOM to figure out where you're losing power. Check for dead mice beneath your fridge—sometimes they get under there and start chewing wires. If you're thoroughly intimidated by electricity, then call a technician.

5-3(e). COMPRESSOR STARTING / ELECTRICAL COMPONENTS

If you *do* hear a sound, it will be something like: "CLICK-BUZZZZZ-ZZZZ-CLICK." The buzz will be between about 5 and 30 seconds long, and it will repeat within a minute or two. What's happening is that your compressor is trying to start, but it can't, and the electrical overload is cycling on and off. It might be that one of your compressor starting components is bad, or that your compressor motor is wearing or worn out.

With modern, solid-state starting components such as those pictured in figure 36a, you may not hear clicking and buzzing as you do with older machines. If there is power to the components, but the compressor won't start, either the compressor or starting components are bad.

Figure 36: Removing Compressor Starting Components

Thermal Overload

Spring Retainer usually fits in slots

Terminals

Compressor Leads

Remove the components by pulling them straight off the terminals

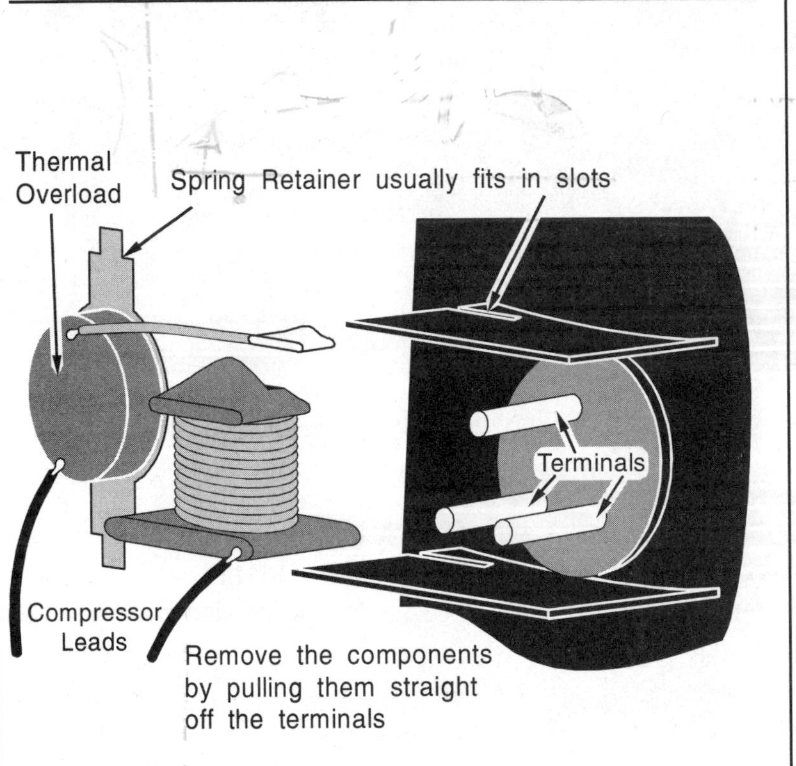

Figure 36a: Typical Solid State Starting Components

Wire leads plug onto terminals

Overload

Relay

Components plug directly onto compressor terminals

You may be able to test each starting component and replace the bad one. However, I've found that the quickest and easiest way to diagnose this problem is to replace all three with a solid state "3-in-1" unit, or just replace all the components. They aren't that expensive.

In the parts houses, "3-in-1" units are also known as "hard start" units. They contain circuitry that provides a little extra power to start a hard-starting compressor.

First, remove the old starting components. (See Figure 36) Note carefully how they came off, in case you need to re-install them. Install the "3-in-1" using the instructions that come with it. (Figure 37). You can use your alligator jumpers to wire it in temporarily. Make sure the "3-in-1" you get is rated for the horsepower of your compressor.

If your refrigerator has solid state starting components, the "3-in-1" may fit onto your fridge directly, or it may not fit at all. If your case is the latter, you will need to get the original equipment replacement relay assembly for your fridge.

If your compressor doesn't start with the "3-in-1," the compressor's dead. You will hear the overload in the "3-in-1" cycling (CLICK-BUZZZZ-CLICK.) It's time to call a tech for a compressor job, or to think about getting a new fridge.

If your refrigerator *does* start, unplug the refrigerator and wire your "3-in-1" in permanently. Use butt connectors, wire nuts and electrical tape. Make sure

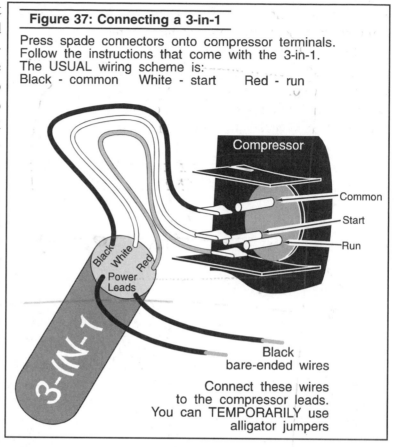

Figure 37: Connecting a 3-in-1

Press spade connectors onto compressor terminals. Follow the instructions that come with the 3-in-1. The USUAL wiring scheme is:
Black - common   White - start   Red - run

Compressor

Common
Start
Run

Black White Red
Power Leads

3-IN-1

Black
bare-ended wires

Connect these wires to the compressor leads. You can TEMPORARILY use alligator jumpers

that none of the compressor terminals are touching each other or the metal housing of the compressor. Also make sure you cover the compressor terminals with a shield; usually you can use the old plastic relay cover and just lead the wires into it.

If the *cause* of your compressor's not starting was bad starting components, it will continue to run indefinitely.

If the cause of it not starting was that the compressor motor is getting worn out, the "3-in-1" will prolong the life of your compressor for somewhere between a few hours and a year or two.

You have no way of knowing which it was, or how long it will last, without some expensive tests that probably won't tell you much anyway. Count your blessings and start saving up for a new fridge (or a major repair), just in case.

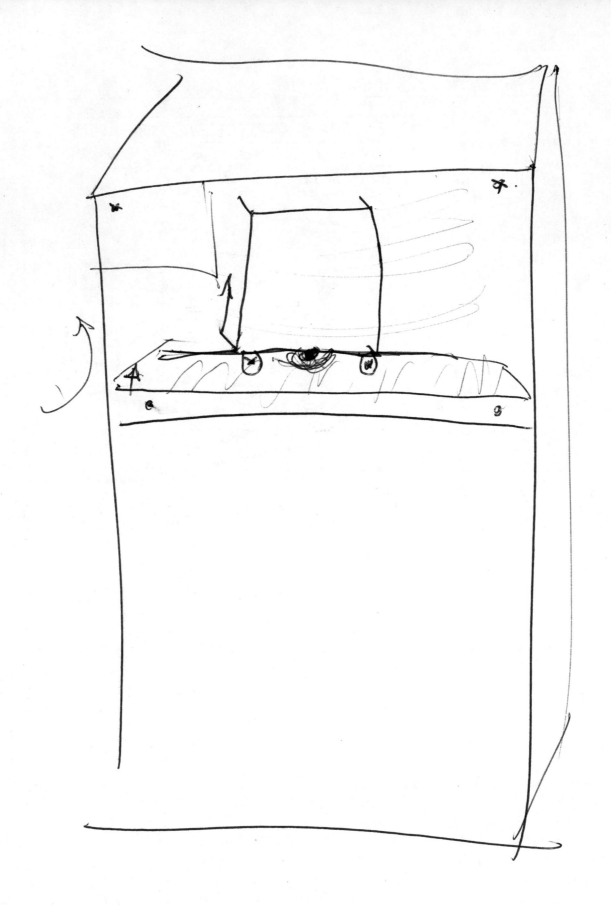

Chapter 6

ICE OR WATER BUILDUP

If you have water build-up on the floor of the food compartment, or ice buildup on the floor of the freezer compartment, you are probably suffering from either a frost problem (see section 4-4) *or* from a clogged defrost drain. There *are* a few exceptions described in section 7-7.

6-1. DEFROST DRAIN SYSTEM

Directly beneath the evaporator will be a water collection pan with a drain hole. Leading from that drain hole to the drain pan beneath your refrigerator is a drain tube.

Side-by-side defrost drain tubes usually go straight down through the freezer floor to the drain pan. (Figure 38)

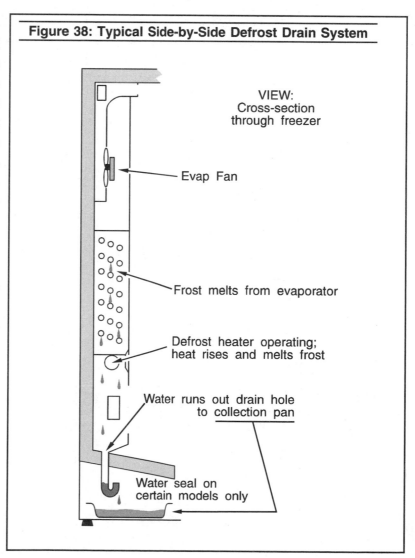

Figure 38: Typical Side-by-Side Defrost Drain System

VIEW:
Cross-section
through freezer

Evap Fan

Frost melts from evaporator

Defrost heater operating; heat rises and melts frost

Water runs out drain hole to collection pan

Water seal on certain models only

Top-freezer models usually drain through a drain tube out the back of the refrigerator and down to the drain pan beneath the fridge (Figure 39). Some top-freezer models have a removable drain tube or trough inside the food compartment. (See Figure 39A)

Some refrigerators, especially older models, may have different defrost drain arrangements. Some top-freezer models drain the defrost water to the inside back wall of the food compartment. The water runs down the back wall to another drain hole which leads outside the fridge to a drain pan. (Figure 40).

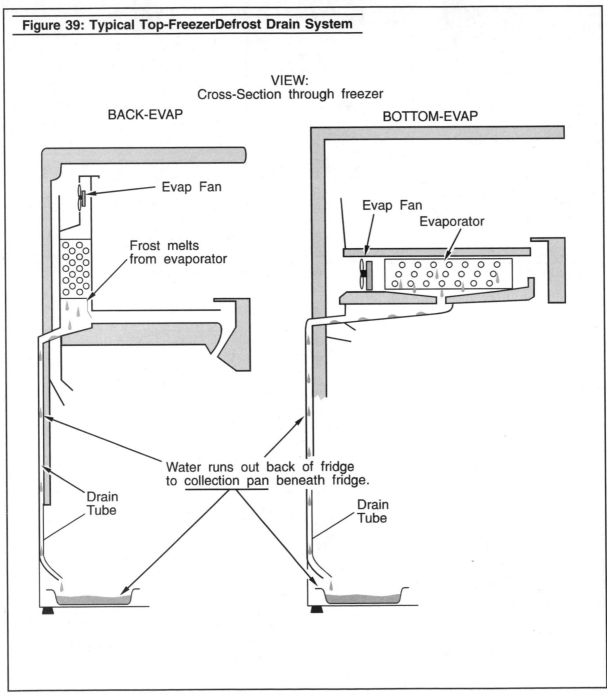

Figure 39: Typical Top-FreezerDefrost Drain System

VIEW:
Cross-Section through freezer

BACK-EVAP

BOTTOM-EVAP

Evap Fan

Frost melts from evaporator

Evap Fan
Evaporator

Water runs out back of fridge to collection pan beneath fridge.

Drain Tube

Drain Tube

**Figure 39A: Removable Defrost Drain Trough
(Certain Top-Freezer Bottom-Evap Models Only)**

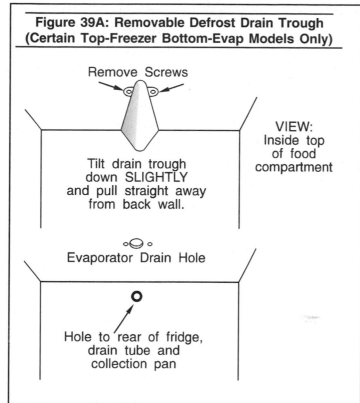

Remove Screws

VIEW:
Inside top
of food
compartment

Tilt drain trough
down SLIGHTLY
and pull straight away
from back wall.

Evaporator Drain Hole

Hole to rear of fridge,
drain tube and
collection pan

6-2. DIAGNOSIS AND REPAIR

On back-evap models, if the drain backs up, it will not freeze the evaporator. You will see the collection pan full and frozen over.

On bottom-evap models, the evaporator will be frozen into one solid block of ice.

In either case, when the collection pan fills up with ice, the defrost water will generally start showing up on the inside floor of your fridge; either as water in a top freezer model or as a thick ice accretion in a side-by-side. The water may leak out onto your kitchen floor, or it may freeze up drawers within the freezer compartment.

Figure 40: Typical Back-Wall Defrost Drain Arrangements (Usually Older Models)

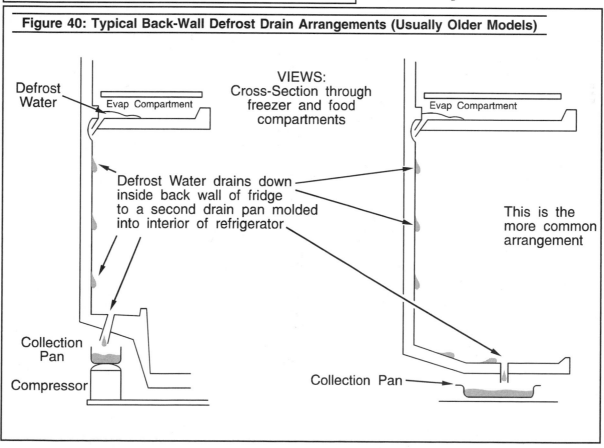

Defrost
Water

VIEWS:
Cross-Section through
freezer and food
compartments

Evap Compartment

Evap Compartment

Defrost Water drains down
inside back wall of fridge
to a second drain pan molded
into interior of refrigerator.

This is the
more common
arrangement

Collection
Pan

Compressor

Collection Pan

In a top-freezer model, you will probably also see ice or drippy water on the roof of the food compartment.

Any ice or water must be removed and/ or melted and the drains cleared. The fastest way to do this is to melt the ice with a blow dryer and to blow the drains clear with a pan of hot water and a syringe-type turkey baster. (Figure 41)

You will need to remove the evaporator panel to access the defrost drain. (See Section 4-2.)

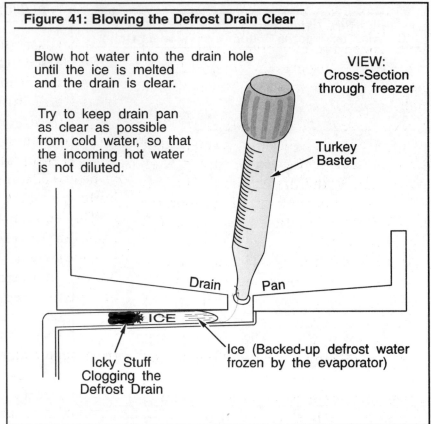

Figure 41: Blowing the Defrost Drain Clear

Blow hot water into the drain hole until the ice is melted and the drain is clear.

Try to keep drain pan as clear as possible from cold water, so that the incoming hot water is not diluted.

VIEW: Cross-Section through freezer

Turkey Baster

Drain   Pan

ICE

Ice (Backed-up defrost water frozen by the evaporator)

Icky Stuff Clogging the Defrost Drain

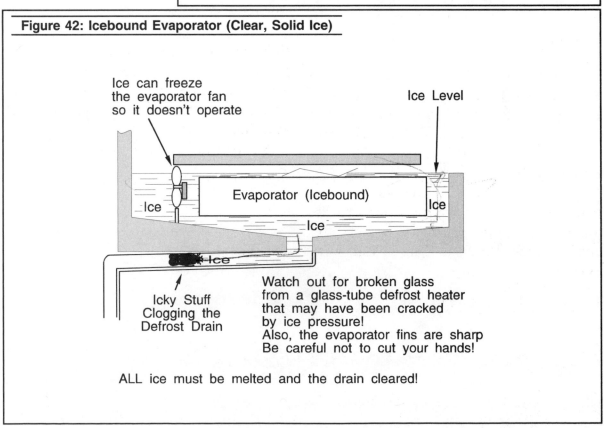

Figure 42: Icebound Evaporator (Clear, Solid Ice)

Ice can freeze the evaporator fan so it doesn't operate

Ice Level

Evaporator (Icebound)

Ice   Ice

Ice

Ice

Icky Stuff Clogging the Defrost Drain

Watch out for broken glass from a glass-tube defrost heater that may have been cracked by ice pressure!
Also, the evaporator fins are sharp
Be careful not to cut your hands!

ALL ice must be melted and the drain cleared!

Bottom-evap models are a little more difficult. The full collection pan will have frozen the evaporator into a solid block of ice, (Figure 42) which will be a bit more difficult and time-consuming to melt. *You must melt it thoroughly.* Some models have the drain hole located at the very back of the compartment instead of directly beneath the evaporator. Check there first. If the drain hole is not visible, you will need to lift the evaporator as described in Section 4-5(d) to access the drain hole.

If there is a removable drain tube or trough running along the roof of the food compartment to the back of the fridge, remove it so you can get all the ice. (Figure 39A)

As you go along, keep sucking out the excess water (now cold from melting ice) with your turkey baster and put it into an empty pot. This will prevent it from diluting the incoming hot water. It will also prevent it from ending up on your kitchen floor.

Continue blowing hot water into the drain hole until you hear it running into the collection pan beneath your fridge. Give it a few extra blasts of hot water to make sure you get all the ice. Using your turkey baster, empty this collection pan now and then. It will prevent the pan from overflowing onto the floor. If it is too inconvenient or messy to do so, don't worry about it. The water will evaporate eventually.

6-3. DRAIN PAN HEATERS

Some models actually have small heaters attached to the underside of the drain pan. The heater prevents the defrost water from re-freezing and clogging the defrost drain hole when it hits the cold defrost drain pan. If the heater is not working properly, it may have the same effect as a clogged defrost drain, a buildup of ice.

This arrangement is generally used on back-evap fridges (top freezer or side-by-side) where the defrost heater may not be mounted close enough to the drain pan to prevent it from refreezing the drainage. These drain pan heaters are a much lower wattage than the defrost heater and run a bit cooler; when operating, they will feel warm to the touch.

If you have a back-evap model, check the defrost drain pan for a heater. To find it, look for its two power leads. If there *is* a heater, check it for continuity and replace it if it is bad. They are usually held to the pan by spot-welded tubes or clamping plates, or by super-sticky aluminum tape.

Re-assemble your fridge.

Chapter 7

UNUSUAL COMPLAINTS and STORIES FROM THE TRENCHES

Occasionally you will run into an unusual problem that requires you to scratch your head a bit. If you know the basic systems and what they do, you can usually figure out what's going on. Following is a smattering of some of the more unusual or flukey things that I've run into as a home service technician:

7-1. KID CAPERS

If your fridge is warm, always check your controls *first*. Many a time, I was called to someone's house on a "warm fridge" complaint, only to find that the controls had been magically shut off.

When the little *darlings* of the household were *queried* about this divine occurrence, you could literally see the halo forming around their heads. "Did you touch the refrigerator?" Mom would ask. Standing beside the refrigerator that hadn't moved an inch in all of his (or her) six years, the child would inevitably reply: "What refrigerator, Mom?" I'm sure that my soul will burn in hell, but it was no moral dilemma for me to charge the 30 dollar service fee in such cases. One fellow whose unit I "fixed" in this way lost well over 500 dollars worth of meats from his packed-full deep freezer.

Only one time did I see a truly unexplainable occurrence of the controls getting shut off. This was a single lady of about 55 with no kids, who had owned the refrigerator for over 25 years. I'm not trying to harp on kids; it's just that as a home service tech, I've seen a lot of money wasted on unnecessary (and expensive) service calls with suspicious circumstances in homes with kids.

Do yourself a favor; check the controls first. Set them on mid-range settings. You *might* save yourself a lotta time, trouble, and expense.

7-2. THE HOLE-IN-THE-WALL GANG

One of the more perplexing problems that I ran into was a young couple (with 4 or 5 kids) that had a warm fridge. Upon investigation, I discovered that the Freon tubes leading to *and* from the evaporator (*above* it on their side-by-side fridge) were heavily frosted with clear, solid ice. Also, the *wires* leading to the evaporator fan and defrost heater were heavily caked with solid ice. I didn't understand *that* frost pattern at *all*, and I was rushed that day, so I replaced the defrost timer and melted the ice, fully figuring I'd get a callback. Sure enough, five days later, they called me back. Same problem, same weird frost pattern.

I took off the evaporator cover panel and just stood there and STARED at the thing for about ten minutes. (Sometimes that helps me to think. You can't *do* that if the customer is standing there, looking over your shoulder. But *he* was at work, and *she* was busy with her kids.) I was just trying to think of where all that moisture could be coming from.

Suddenly, I noticed a hole, about 1" in diameter, in the upper left corner of the defrost compartment. I pulled the fridge away from the wall, and saw *daylight* through the hole. It was the pre-drilled hole for the icemaker water tube. (They did not have an icemaker, but most modern fridges come pre-drilled and wired for icemakers in case you ever want to install one.) Warm, humid air was feeding straight into the evaporator compartment!! I asked the lady about it. She said that her husband, just messing around, had pulled the little cover off the back of the fridge "about two weeks

ago." I stuffed the little hole with some bubble-pack that I just happened to have around and duct-taped both sides to seal the hole.

Ignorance really *can* cost you. But at least the kids didn't do it this time.

7-3. DOOR SEALS AND ALIGNMENT

I personally think that door seals are one of the most misunderstood pieces of the refrigerator. Ask a do-it-yourselfer about why his fridge is warm, and the first thing he'll say after "I don't do Freon" is "but let's check the door seals." Door seals *rarely* have problems over the life of the fridge. The only ones I've seen go bad are in households that have dogs or cats that like to chew or sharpen their claws on them, or kids (there's those pesky *kids* again) that like to climb or hang on the refrigerator door. A *really* bad door seal problem is *most* likely to show up as a *defrost* problem, due to humid air getting into the fridge.

Door seals are magnetically held to the door frame and mullions. (See Figure 43 for a typical cross-section.) Unless the seal is shredded or you can physically see a gap between the seal and the door frame with the door closed, there is no reason to suspect a door seal problem.

To replace the seal, you must have a nut driver of the proper size. A power cordless drill-driver is better. A magnetic tip may prevent you from going crazy trying to hold the driver, the screw and the seal at the same time. There are lot of screws holding the seal on. Remove the screws from NO MORE THAN two sides at a time. One side at a time is better. The idea is to prevent the plastic inner door liner (or shelving) from

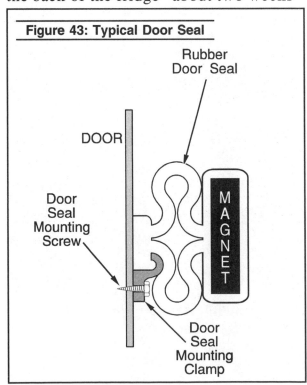

Figure 43: Typical Door Seal

Rubber Door Seal

DOOR

Door Seal Mounting Screw

MAGNET

Door Seal Mounting Clamp

drifting around—if you have to re-align it, it can be a long, frustrating, trial-and-error process. The new seal will fit in the same way as the old one came out.

You are much more likely to have a door *alignment* problem or warping. There's not much you can do with a badly warped door except to try to warp it back into shape, or replace it.

With the door closed, measure the gap around it; top and bottom, left and right. Check if the door edges and refrigerator edges are parallel. If the measurements indicate that the door is badly out of alignment, re-align it be loosening the hinges slightly (one hinge at a time) and shifting the door around. It may take a few tries to get it aligned properly.

Remove anything obstructing the seals. Sometimes the kick plate will get in the way. If it's metal, you may be able to bend it slightly to solve your problem.

7-4. MOVING DAY

If you have to move your fridge for any reason, make sure that you keep it upright. If you turn it on its side there's a strong probability that the compressor oil will run out of the compressor and into the condenser, and when you start the fridge, the compressor will burn out within a few hours or even minutes, for lack of lubrication. I've heard of people getting lucky and getting away with it; maybe they just *happened* to lay it on the "lucky" side of the fridge. It's not worth the risk. If your fridge has been laid on its side, stand it upright again but don't plug it in for a day or two. Just hope that either the oil drains back into the compressor or that it didn't run out in the first place.

7-5. A SHOCKING EXPERIENCE (MULLION HEATERS)

Once I was called to the home of a little old dog-breeder who had complained of being *shocked* while opening his refrigerator door. When I arrived, I couldn't feel anything at all—until once I happened to be leaning against the metal door of his oven (opposite his fridge) when I touched his door—ZAP! I put a volt meter between the two doors and discovered 50 volts!!

It turned out that the mullion (anti-sweat) heater (see section 4-1) in his door had shorted, and was grounding wherever it could—right through *him* to the oven door. Since this happened in a not-too-humid environment, the solution was simple. I disabled the heater by disconnecting and insulating the heater leads at the base of the door, where they went into the fridge. This story is made even more interesting by the fact that the little old dog-breeder's wife had just had open-heart surgery and a pacemaker installed *three weeks* before. I shudder to think what could have happened had *she* touched the fridge.

Another interesting observation about mullion heaters is that if your fridge starts to become warm, one of the first signs *may* be that the door jamb start to feel downright *hot*. This happens when the refrigerator is no longer removing heat from the doorframe and the mullion heater inside. This is especially prevalent in the doorframe between the food and freezer compartment in a side-by-side.

7-6 MICE CAPADES

A few years back, where I lived in Southern California, we had a nasty cold spell; I mean, it was well below 45 degrees every day for a *week*. (Eat your hearts out, Midwesterners.) About a week later, I got a call from a lady with a warm fridge. Upon investigation, I found that a mouse, apparently seeking the warmth of the compressor, had crawled into there and died (whether from the heat of the compressor or from getting struck by the condenser fan, I don't know.) Anyway, he got stuck to the floor pan near the condenser fan and as he dried out, his feet and tail curled up until they finally got stuck in and stopped the condenser fan. In the home-service biz, you learn to start looking for animal and insect problems after a cold spell; lizards in the dryer vent, birds that fly into the oven roof vent and get baked and jam your oven hood exhaust fan—stuff like that.

Another neat trick that animals (especially rodents, but sometimes cats, too) like to play is to get under the fridge and start chewing wires or insulation. This can cause electrical problems, or loose insulation might get caught in the condenser fan. Cats have been known to tear off the bottom back panel of the fridge. This disturbs the airflow over the condenser and may jam the condenser fan with fiberglass insulation.

7-7 ICEMAKERS AND IN-DOOR WATER DISPENSERS

If you start to get an unusual buildup of ice in one particular spot in your freezer, especially beneath the icemaker, check for water leaks.

Water leaking onto the kitchen floor *not* traceable to one of the problems in Chapters 4 or 6 *may* be from a leak in the icemaker or door dispenser water system. Icemakers have a water solenoid valve mounted on the back of the fridge, usually behind the back bottom panel, and a water tube that leads straight up the back of the fridge to the icemaker. Door dispensers have a similar water solenoid valve with a water tube that leads beneath the fridge and into the door through a hollow hinge. If your fridge has *both* features, it's usually a dual water solenoid valve. It *can* be simple or not-so-simple to fix, but basically it's just a plumbing job.

7-8 SEE THE LIGHT

On several occasions, I have been called to peoples' homes with the complaint that the freezer or food section was cold in the bottom, but felt like a warming oven was on in the top of the compartment.

It turned out in every case that the interior lights were not shutting off. (A light bulb puts out enough heat to actually *warm* the top of the compartment. Remember, warm air rises.) There are two things that might cause this.

One is a defective door switch, easily diagnosed and corrected.

The other is if nothing is *contacting* the door switch. Some units were built with a removable interior shelf that also shut off the light by contacting the door switch. Remove the shelf, and nothing hits the switch; the light doesn't turn off.

The easiest way to diagnose this is to peek into the compartment while slowly closing the door. If the light does not shut off well before the door is fully closed, test the switch and look at its closing mechanism and see what's happening.

7-9. BAD ODORS

To my experience, this is one of the toughest problems to solve. I have been called out on a variety of "bad odor" complaints, and rarely are they solvable. Modern fridges, with few exceptions, have plastic interiors that *do* absorb odors to some degree, rather than the porcelain interiors standard in days of yore. If you have an odor problem, it *may* help to keep an open box of baking soda in there, or to wash out the interior of the fridge with a very mild bleach solution.

If your fridge has had a meltdown (thawed out with everything in it), try pulling off whatever panels you can and see if any meat blood or other smelly stuff has gotten under them. Styrofoam panels can absorb odors, too—but try washing with a mild soap solution.

One semi-solvable odor problem that I ran into was a fellow whose fire-engine red fridge was getting warm *and* it had an absolutely acrid smell within. It turned out that the defrost heater lead within the defrost compartment had shorted out and burned off a bunch of its heavy rubber insulation, then melted itself so the defrost system was not working. I fixed the fridge, but I do not know if he ever got out the burnt-rubber smell.

7-10. FIX THE LITTLE STUFF

Have you had a broken door catch or handle? For *years*? A light bulb out? How about the kickplate—how long has *it* been falling off? Maybe you have a missing shelf, or one shelf that's cracked. *You* know the one I'm talking about; every time you put something on that shelf, you have to do a quick mental weight and stress calculation to make sure everything on it doesn't end up on the kitchen floor. It's *really* annoying to think about, isn't it? So naturally, you just stop thinking about it.

Take the time to make it right! Plastic parts are usually not that expensive; though things like shelves usually must be gotten through the dealer or factory warehouse. Special appliance light bulbs are a couple of bucks at your nearest appliance parts dealer. How much is your peace of mind worth?

7-11 STRANGE NOISES

Actually, there aren't too many things in a fridge that can cause a lot of noise. A few that you might commonly hear are:

*A **rattling or a buzzing noise*** might be coming from the evaporator or condenser fan hitting something. It may also be that the defrost drain pan or compressor mounts are loose and something is vibrating a bit.

*A **whistling or warbling sound*** usually is coming from the evaporator fan motor. Replace as described in section 4-3.

*A **hissing or gurgling sound*** might happen for a few minutes after the compressor shuts off. This is the Freon flowing through the tubing in the system. When the pressure throughout the system equalizes, the noise will stop. If there is no evaporator fan running, you *may* hear the Freon gurgling through the evaporator at any time the fridge is running.

7-12. FIRE IN THE FRIDGE!!!

Okay, *you're* the tech. You get a frantic call from a customer saying there's a red glow in the bottom of the freezer in his side-by-side; he's afraid that something's burning. He doesn't hear it running, but he does hear popping and hissing noises. You rush over to his home, and when you get there, you don't see any red glow. You *do* notice that the light doesn't work in the freezer. He says that it went out months ago, and he hasn't gotten around to replacing it. He has had the fridge for ten years, and has never seen a red glow down there before. What do you do?

If you're me, you grab a screwdriver, reach down to the defrost timer and set it on "defrost" again. Then you reach into your tool kit for your trusty, dusty extendable inspection mirror. You show the customer, via the mirror, the red-glowing defrost heater. You explain the defrost system and why he's never noticed a red glow before:

When the light bulb was working, the interior of the fridge was *so* bright that he just couldn't *see* that dim red glow. And the defrost heater is only *on* for about 10 or 15 minutes every 6 to 8 hours. What are the odds against his opening the fridge at *just* the right time and seeing the fridge in a defrost cycle?

Then you sell him a special appliance light bulb for three-fifty, plus a second one as a spare, and you charge him a 30-dollar service call fee besides.

As I said before, ignorance *truly can* cost you.

Chapter 8

DOMESTIC ICEMAKERS

8-1 ICEMAKER TYPES

Icemakers are divided into two basic types; flex-tray and hard tray. (Figure A-1)

FLEX-TRAY

Flex-tray icemakers have a flexible plastic ice mold, or "tray," similar to manual ice molds. Also like manual molds, when it comes time to eject (harvest) the ice from the mold, it inverts and twists, "popping" out the ice. The tray then turns back upright and refills with water for the next freeze cycle.

HARD-TRAY

Hard-tray icemakers have a metal ice mold which is coated with a non-stick coating. The ice mold remains upright, and cubes are ejected by some mechanical device which pushes the ice out of the mold and into the ice bin.

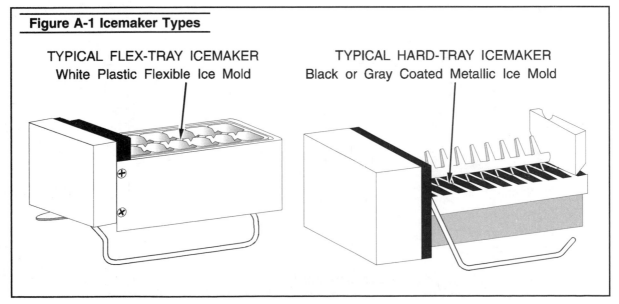

Figure A-1 Icemaker Types

TYPICAL FLEX-TRAY ICEMAKER
White Plastic Flexible Ice Mold

TYPICAL HARD-TRAY ICEMAKER
Black or Gray Coated Metallic Ice Mold

8-1(a) ICEMAKER OPERATION

The operation of the icemaker can be broken down into three cycles; the freeze cycle, the harvest cycle and the fill cycle.

FREEZE CYCLE

The freeze cycle begins after the mold has filled with water. It ends when the water is completely frozen into cubes and the harvest cycle begins. The amount of time spent in the freeze cycle is controlled by a number of factors depending on the individual design, but it is best explained by knowing how the harvest cycle is triggered.

HARVEST CYCLE

The harvest cycle occurs when the ice is ejected from the ice mold. (Figure A-2) The harvest cycle is triggered in one of two ways, depending on whether the icemaker has a flexible ice mold, (flex-tray) or a rigid metal ice mold. (hard-tray)

FLEX-TRAY HARVEST CYCLE

Most flex-tray icemakers harvest ice solely on the basis of accumulated time, or "run" time. Timing is accomplished by a low-rpm icemaker drive motor acting through reduction gears. Every two hours or so of "run" time, depending on the design, the icemaker harvests. However, it should be noted that the accumulation of "run" time is, in one way or another, thermostatically controlled. For example, Admiral-type flex-tray machines have a thermostat in line with the icemaker timing and drive motor that opens at 19 degrees, and doesn't close again till the freezer temperature drops to 15 degrees. Therefore, time only accumulates if the temperature drops below 15 degrees. Whirlpool flex-tray icemakers accumulate time only while the compressor is running, which is determined by the cold control, which is the thermostat that controls the refrigerator and freezer temperatures.

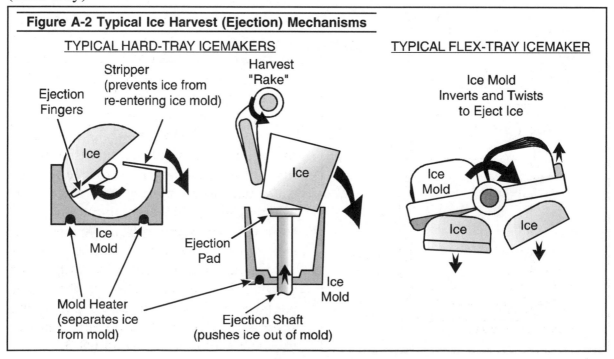

Figure A-2 Typical Ice Harvest (Ejection) Mechanisms

TYPICAL HARD-TRAY ICEMAKERS

Ejection Fingers

Stripper (prevents ice from re-entering ice mold)

Harvest "Rake"

Ice

Ice

Ice Mold

Ejection Pad

Ice Mold

Mold Heater (separates ice from mold)

Ejection Shaft (pushes ice out of mold)

TYPICAL FLEX-TRAY ICEMAKER

Ice Mold Inverts and Twists to Eject Ice

Ice Mold

Ice

Ice

HARD TRAY HARVEST CYCLE

In hard-tray icemakers, harvest is triggered thermostatically. A thermostat pressed against the ice mold senses that it is cold enough to ensure that the ice is frozen. (For example, the thermostat on the late model modular crescent-cube machine closes at 17 degrees F.) When the thermostat closes, the drive motor activates, and the harvest begins.

When the harvest cycle begins in hard-tray icemakers, a heater begins slowly heating the ice mold. When the harvest mechanism contacts the ice, it stalls until the ice melts enough to release it from the mold. Though the surface of the cube does liquefy slightly, it refreezes quickly. Cubes in the bin might occasionally stick together a little bit because of this liquefication, but they should be easy to separate.

In a hard-tray icemaker, the thermostat *starts* the harvest cycle, but it does not *end* the cycle. The mold heater would open the thermostat and end the cycle *way* too early; long before the mold was refilled. When the thermostat begins the harvest cycle, a cam attached to the drive motor closes a "holding" switch. This switch keeps the drive motor turning until the ice is harvested and the mold refills with water. When the ejection mechanism is reset, the mold is refilled and the cam reaches the proper position, the cam allows the holding switch to open. This ends the fill cycle and begins the freeze cycle.

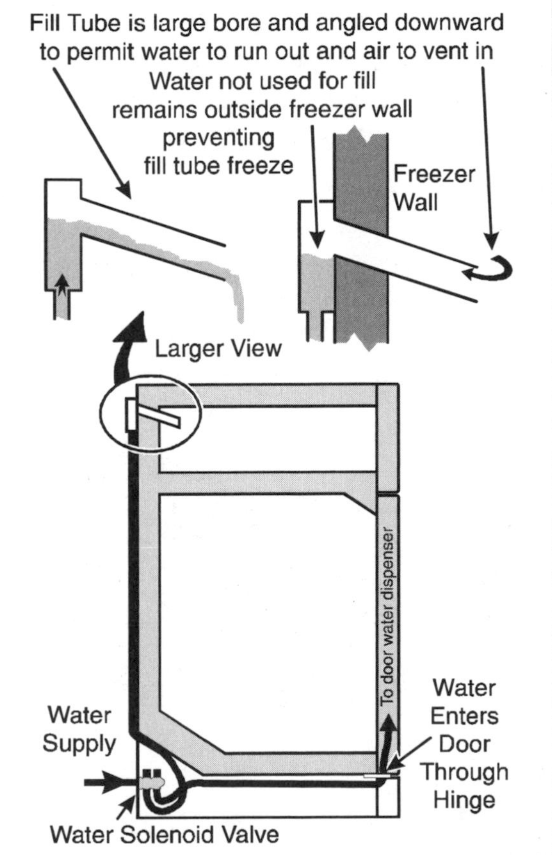

FILL CYCLE AND FILL VALVE

Towards the end of the harvest cycle, a cam on the drive mechanism closes the fill switch. This switch opens a fill solenoid valve, usually located on the back of the fridge, at the bottom. (Figure A-3) In refrigerators with water dispensers in the door, a *dual* water solenoid valve is used. One controls water to the door dispenser and the other controls water to the icemaker.

The amount of water that enters the ice mold is controlled by a couple of things. The shape of the cam that closes the fill switch controls the length of time the valve stays open. A flow control washer within the valve adjusts the flow for variations in house water pressure, so that the same amount of water flows through the valve regardless of water pressure. However, if the water pressure is below about 20 psi at the solenoid valve inlet, problems can occur; see sections 8-2(a) and 8-3.

Figure A-3 Typical Fill Water System

Fill Tube is large bore and angled downward to permit water to run out and air to vent in
Water not used for fill remains outside freezer wall preventing fill tube freeze

Freezer Wall

Larger View

Water Supply

To door water dispenser

Water Enters Door Through Hinge

Water Solenoid Valve

8-2 DIAGNOSING PROBLEMS

One of the reasons that icemakers can be so dog-gone tough to diagnose is the simple observation that ice takes an hour or two to freeze in a freezer. After a repair, you can't stand there with the freezer door open, waiting for the next harvest cycle, to make sure the machine is working properly. Symptoms may take time to develop and recur if the machine is not fixed the first time. Most icemakers are temperature-sensitive, and as the freezer temperature rises and falls, this sensitivity can cause symptoms to be intermittent.

Icemakers can behave erratically, and be difficult to diagnose because of it. But a basic understanding of how a particular design operates can go a long way towards removing the mystery of intermittent malfunctions. Before you start working, *observe the symptoms* of the malfunction. Knowing how the icemaker *should* operate may point you towards what *isn't* operating correctly.

Has the fridge or freezer seemed warmer or colder than usual? This can point towards refrigerator problems other than the icemaker, such as defrost or sealed system problems. Freezer temperature in most cases should be between 0 and 15 degrees Farenheit. Any higher, and the ice may not freeze fast enough or the thermostat may not trigger a harvest cycle. Any lower, and the cold may migrate into the refrigerator compartment.

Has the freezer or refrigerator door been opened a lot? In some circumstances, this can keep the freezer temperature too high and cause slow or no ice production, or "shelling," where the cube has not frozen completely before the harvest cycle begins.

Do not yet discard any "slabbed" ice. The *way* the ice is slabbing can help tip you off to the cause of the problem. For example, ice cubes fused together at the top can indicate an overfill or levelling problems; ice slabbed in the bin can indicate shelling, ice mold leakage, or a variety of other problems.

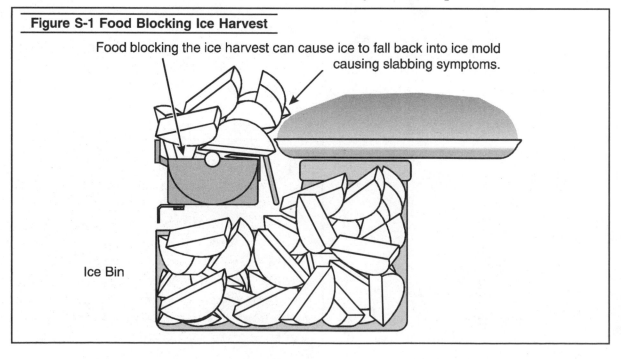

Figure S-1 Food Blocking Ice Harvest

Food blocking the ice harvest can cause ice to fall back into ice mold causing slabbing symptoms.

Ice Bin

SYMPTOMS

Icemaker complaints seem to be generally divided into five main symptoms.

A) Ice cubes taste or smell bad. See section 8-3, water supply problems.

B) The ice is "slabbing;" cubes are freezing together into blocks in the bin. See section 8-2(a).

C) "Hollow" cubes. The ice cubes are "shelling," or not freezing completely before the harvest cycle tries to eject them from the mold. See section 8-2(b).

D) The fill tube keeps filling with ice and blocking the flow of fill water. See section 8-2(c).

E) The icemaker is not working at all, or is producing ice very slowly. See section 8-4.

8-2(a) SLABBING

This generally occurs when the ice is not ejecting from the ice mold properly. If there are cubes left in the ice mold after a harvest cycle, the new waterfill will overfill the mold for the next batch. Depending on the design, this may cause the mold to overflow, or it may just cause a thick sheet of ice to fuse together the tops of the cubes too solidly. In this case, the icemaker can jam and the problem can compound itself rapidly.

This can be caused by a number of factors. One of the big culprits is freezer food placed too close to the icemaker. This can simply prevent the ice from dropping into the bin, (Figure S-1) or it can interfere with the ice level sensor arm, preventing the icemaker from shutting off when the bin is full. (Figure S-2) In this case, the solution would be to clear the excess ice and — ***don't do it again!!!***

Figure S-2 Trapped Feeler (Ice Level) Arm

Ice level feeler arm rises during harvest and prevents further harvest if ice bin is full

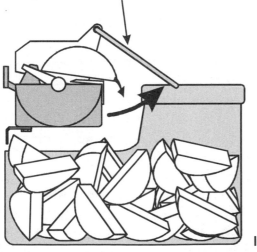

If feeler arm is blocked by ice or food harvest will continue with the bin full and slabbing symptoms can develop.

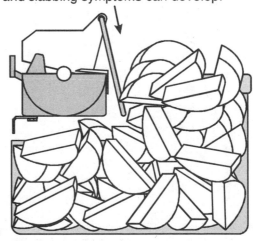

Ice Bin

Another culprit can be that the surface of the mold is too rough for the ice to properly eject. (Figure S-3) This may be caused by hard water calcium buildup, scale or corrosion of the ice mold surface. Both hard-tray and flex-tray machines are prone to this problem; it is caused by impurities in the fill water. (see section 8-3) In hard-tray machines, the ice mold surface coating may actually separate from the metal mold itself. The problem can get so bad that you may see black or gray flakes and sediment in the cubes. In both hard- and flex-tray machines, the solution is usually to replace the ice mold, or just the entire icemaker. In some circumstances, scale can be removed with a weak solution of lime cleaner. If you do this, rinse the mold with a weak chlorine bleach solution and flush with copious amounts of water before you put

the mold back into service. If possible, try to get a better hard water filtration system installed in the icemaker water supply.

LOW WATER PRESSURE

Water supply pressure below about 20 psi can cause low water fill and small cube size. Sometimes, some cubes may not eject properly and may stay in the mold. The next fill will then cause overfill, and slabbing symptoms may develop.

Low water pressure can also cause the valve to leak, sometimes badly enough to overfill or overflow the ice mold. However, this particular problem *usually* shows up as an ice-blocked fill tube. See Section 8-2(c), section 8-3 and Figure S-4.

8-2(b) SHELLING

Hollow cubes, or "shelling" can occur if the ice cubes are not fully frozen when the harvest cycle begins. The causes and effects of shelling vary. Depending on the design, either the harvest cycle is being triggered prematurely, or the cube is not freezing in the allotted time.

Shelling may be an early sign of defrost, sealed system or other cooling problems of the refrigerator itself, especially in flex-tray machines. Check the freezer temperature.

In flex-tray machines with shelling symptoms, water pouring from the ice mold during the harvest cycle may freeze the bin into a solid block from the bottom up (slabbing.) Slush left in the ice mold may also cause overfill. The freezer vents in flex-tray machines must direct cold air directly at the sur-

Figure S-3 Ice Mold Deposits
Look for calcium or other deposits or any roughness to the surface of the ice mold. Also feel the surface with your fingertips; white calcium deposits can be difficult to see against the white plastic surface of the mold.

face of the water or the mold, to insure that it will freeze in the alloted time. Check that nothing is blocking the air-stream and that the freezer vent directing air over the icemaker is not damaged, missing or misdirected.

In hard-tray machines with shelling symptoms, ice or water left in the mold after harvest may cause overfill and slabbing problems. Shelling is usually a sign of low waterfill, which allows the mold to get colder faster, triggering the thermostat into a harvest cycle too quickly. Check and adjust the water level (sections 8-5 thru 8-8) or check for low water pressure or the incorrect water valve. (section 8-3(b)) There is a baffle kit for late model Whirlpool crescent-cube machines with shelling problems, that redirects air over the ice to freeze it more quickly.

8-2(c) BLOCKED (FROZEN) FILL TUBE

If the fill tube gets choked up with ice, (Figure S-4) it usually means that the water fill solenoid valve is leaking. The valve is not closing properly and is dribbling water. If the leakage is slow enough, water may freeze in the fill tube. Over time it will freeze the tube completely shut.

To melt the ice from the tube and clear it, you can use a blow dryer, or blow hot water into the tube with a turkey baster. Hot water is faster but usually a little messier. Put a couple of towels and/or a pan below the tube to catch the water runoff.

You should replace the solenoid valve (be sure to read through section 8-3(b)). However, this may not be the whole solution. Wear and tear *may* have caused the valve to leak, but not necessarily. Sediment from improper installation or low water pressure may prevent the valve from closing fully. If you have this symptom, especially if it returns after clearing the ice blockage once, start checking for water supply pressure or sediment problems. See Section 8-3, water supply problems.

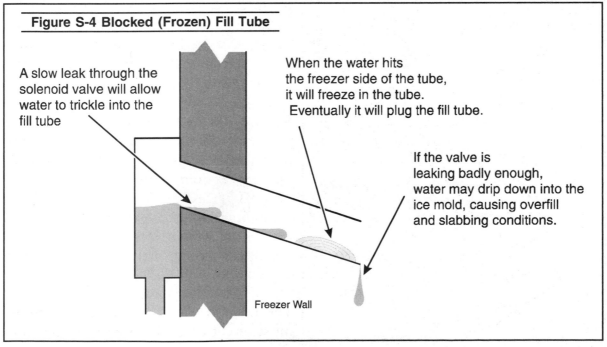

Figure S-4 Blocked (Frozen) Fill Tube

A slow leak through the solenoid valve will allow water to trickle into the fill tube

When the water hits the freezer side of the tube, it will freeze in the tube. Eventually it will plug the fill tube.

If the valve is leaking badly enough, water may drip down into the ice mold, causing overfill and slabbing conditions.

Freezer Wall

8-3 WATER SOURCE

A commonly overlooked cause of many problems is an inadequate water supply. Water supply problems can cause a variety of symptoms. Sediment or odor in the ice, water solenoid valve problems and even inoperation or slow operation of the icemaker itself can be traced to water supply problems. *I cannot stress enough the **importance** of having an **adequate, properly filtered water supply!!!***

Of particular concern is the source of the water.

Ideally, the system should come directly from cold-water copper piping in the house. I've seen people tap into hot water pipes, but the piping should be long enough so that water does not fill the icemaker while hot, or the water may not freeze fast enough. It is far better to use a cold water line if possible.

"Saddle valves" are often used on a new installation to pierce into an existing pipe, (Figure F-1) and generally work pretty well. However, you must be careful of using dissimilar metals; for example a copper valve on a galvanized steel pipe. A water supply drawn from a saddle valve on a galvanized pipe is an invitation to scale and sediment problems.

Similarly, a saddle valve installed too close to a hot water tank can pick up calcium sediments from the tank itself. Scale and sediments can block the saddle valve and cause low water flow.

Low water flow through the saddle valve may cause the same symptoms as low water pressure at the solenoid valve inlet. (see section 8-2(a)) If unfiltered, these impurities can also cause

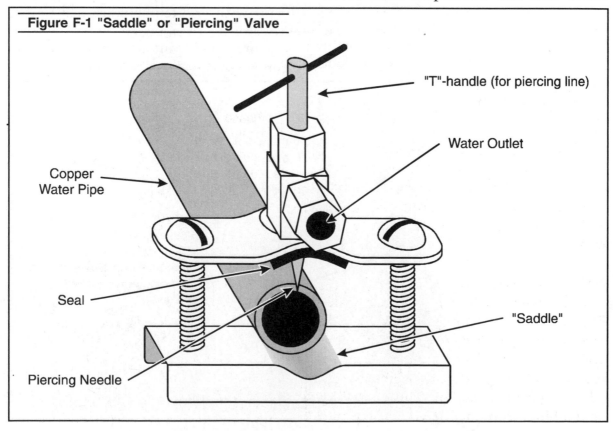

Figure F-1 "Saddle" or "Piercing" Valve

"T"-handle (for piercing line)

Water Outlet

Copper Water Pipe

Seal

"Saddle"

Piercing Needle

poor quality ice. They can also get into the solenoid valve seat and prevent the valve from closing fully, causing symptoms from fill tube freeze to slabbing. (see below)

If your system uses a saddle valve, and has low pressure symptoms as described in section 8-2(a), you may be able to temporarily knock some of the sediment loose by "exercising," or opening and closing the saddle valve a number of times. Also replace the solenoid valve, especially if the supply line is unfiltered. However, the only long term solution is to secure a better supply, directly from a copper cold-water pipe if possible. And use the proper filtration for the water in your house, or at *least* a sediment filter.

PIPING: COPPER OR PLASTIC?

I prefer plastic. It's a little cheaper, easier to cut and install, and less prone to leakage when you have to move the refrigerator. However, some people feel it's more prone to leakage than copper simply because the material is stronger. That's not been my experience, but it's your call.

If you do use plastic, make sure you insert the brass sleeves into the ends (Figure F-2) before installing the compression fittings. Without them, the ends of the plastic could collapse and leak.

HOT WATER OR COLD?

I've seen people tap into hot water lines to feed the icemaker, but I highly recommend **against** it. You definitely don't want hot water actually *entering* the icemaker mold; the water would take longer to freeze and cause shelling or slabbing problems. If you do tap into

a hot water line for the icemaker supply, make sure there's a nice, long run of water tube before it gets to the refrigerator, to allow time for the water inside the line to cool between fills. Install a couple of loops of tube if you have to. Also, use copper line; it conducts heat better and is more resistant to heat damage than plastic.

One amusing little anecdote that I read on the internet was about an individual who piped hot water to his icemaker, reasoning that "hot water freezes faster." Well, heat flow *is* greater when the temperature difference is greater, so the heat will actually flow out of the water and into the freezer faster *while the water is hot*. But when the temperature of the water drops, the heat flow slows to the same rate as if you had just filled it with cool water in the first place. And since, to begin with, the temperature has further to go, it takes *longer* to freeze hot water!

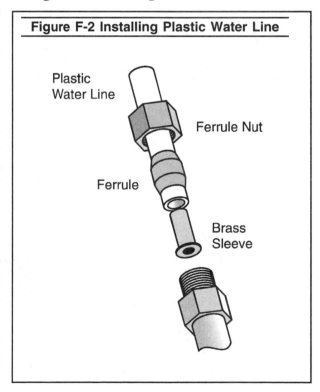

Figure F-2 Installing Plastic Water Line

Plastic Water Line

Ferrule Nut

Ferrule

Brass Sleeve

8-3(a) FILTRATION & PURIFICATION

Water filtration is a subject for a whole book unto itself. Common complaints and contaminants are chlorine, rust, sand, dirt, sediment, dissolved calcium, organic substances such as PCB's, THM's, herbicides and pesticides, chloramines and detergents, causing bad taste, odors or even health hazards. This book is not intended to be a primer on water filtration; I would in no way *begin* to *try* to *pretend* to be able advise you what contaminants you need to guard against in your area. For that, you need to hire a water chemist, or talk to your water company or neighbors who might have been through this already. You might even try talking to your appliance parts dealer; he may know what local conditions are and carry the correct filtration elements.

However, as a *bare minimum*, you should filter out dirt, sand, rust and sediment. These contaminants you can pick up independent of what your water company supplies you, through old or inadequate water piping or other house conditions. This applies even (especially!) to brand new homes. Ever seen a pallet load of pipe laying on a construction lot? You don't think the pipefitters washed all the bugs and dirt out of the tubing before they brazed it in place, do you?

INLINE AND UNDER-SINK (CARTRIDGE) FILTERS
(Figures F-3 and F-4)

In my opinion, about the only good thing about inline filters (vs. cartridge-type filters) is that the initial cost tends to be quite a bit less.

However, inline filters are harder to change; usually you have to cut the old one out and pipe the new one in. Being behind the fridge instead of under the sink, they are harder to get to, and easier to *forget* to change.

Cartridge-type filters, on the other hand, have replaceable cartridges which are relatively easy to get to and change. Some even have water shutoff valves built right into them to make filter changing even faster and easier. They are little, if any, more difficult to install initially, and replacement cartridges usually cost less than a new inline filter. You can also pipe them fairly easily to a drinking water sink tap if desired.

When installing *either* a new inline water filter or under-sink filter cartridge, especially an activated charcoal

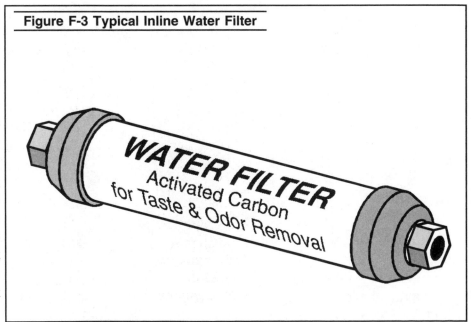

Figure F-3 Typical Inline Water Filter

type, first connect it to the water source. Then run several gallons of water through it until you see the water running clear. Then connect it to the refrigerator. Then, just to be safe, I throw away the ice that it makes for the first 24 hours.

REVERSE OSMOSIS SYSTEMS

Reverse Osmosis water purification systems (commonly referred to as "RO" systems) purify water by forcing it at high pressure through a porous membrane. This removes almost every contaminant whose *molecules* are bigger than water molecules.

The result is extremely clean-tasting water, easily comparable with bottled water.

The down side, aside from initial cost, is that they waste a LOT of water. When the new membrane is new, probably half of the water that enters the RO system goes down the drain to flush the membrane. If you don't change the elements frequently, then when the membrane gets older and plugged with contaminants, as much as 15 to 20 *times* as much water goes down the drain as comes out the faucet. Also, water flows through the RO membrane *very* slowly, so it can drop water pressure at the tap considerably.

Most manufacturers recommend AGAINST an icemaker water supply coming from an RO system. I don't necessarily agree. I have been personally using an RO system on my Whirlpool crescent cube icemaker for two years now and I am tickled with the results; ice as clear and clean tasting as our drinking water, and no scale or calcium deposits. (And I live in an area with VERY hard water.) However, I must qualify my experience on two accounts.

First, unlike some RO systems, mine has a five gallon pressure / holding tank which maintains adequate water supply pressure to the valve at all times.

Second, soft water is relatively acidic, so I am keeping my eyes open for any sign of deterioration of the ice mold coating, and I'm willing to eat an icemaker if it happens. (Beats listening to my wife whine about the yucky tasting ice for a couple of years!)

As a general policy, I'd have to recommend *against* RO purifying the icemaker water. But if you understand the risks, and the RO system doesn't drop the water pressure too low, it can be done.

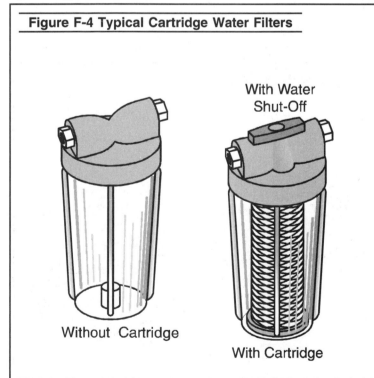

Figure F-4 Typical Cartridge Water Filters

With Water Shut-Off

Without Cartridge

With Cartridge

8-3(b) FILL SOLENOID VALVE

Water fill volume is controlled by a couple of things. For one, the length of time the valve stays open, which is usually controlled by a cam in the icemaker head, which closes a switch for the proper amount of time. A **flow control washer** within the valve adjusts the flow for variations in house water pressure. However, if the water pressure is below about 20 psi at the solenoid valve inlet, problems can occur. Low water pressure can cause low water fill and small cube size. If the cube is too small, it may not eject properly, and the next fill may cause overfill.

Water solenoids operate using a pressure diaphragm with pressure on both sides of the diaphragm. Adequate water pressure is required both to open the solenoid valve and to close it. If the water pressure is low, the valve may not close fully and may leak. Replace any leaking solenoid valve; but be alert for whatever conditions might have caused it to leak in the first place.

A HUGE point of concern is in getting the right water solenoid valve. Different icemakers require a wide variety of fill volumes, from about 3 ounces in certain GE units to as much as 8 ounces in Admiral-type machines. The valve bodies might look the same from the outside, but you must make sure the valve is the correct one (has the correct flow control washer) for the icemaker you're working on. If someone has previously replaced the solenoid valve, and you experience low flow problems or slabbing in an icemaker, double check that the valve is the correct one. If necessary, call your parts supplier and check the part number. This is a **critically** important point.

8-3(c) TESTING AND ADJUSTING FILL VOLUME

To test fill volume, remove the icemaker from its freezer wall mounting (but leave it plugged in) and initiate a harvest cycle if possible. Baby bottles are generally just about the right size for testing fill volume; most are graduated in both cc's and ounces. A good rule of thumb is that one fluid ounce equals about 30 cc's.

Water fill level can be adjusted on *some* icemakers. See sections 8-5 thru 8-8 about your design.

8-4 SLOW OR NO ICE PRODUCTION

There are a number of things that will slow or stop the production of ice. If you are working on an icemaker where you can do so, a good start is to try to manually trigger a harvest cycle and watch what happens. (For triggering instructions, see section 8-5 thru 8-8 about your brand.) To a high degree, the diagnosis depends on the make and model of the icemaker. However, there a few common causes.

8-4(a) FREEZER TEMPERATURE

Check the freezer temperature. Use a calibration thermometer, available cheaply in most appliance parts stores. In most icemakers, a freezer temperature above about 15 degrees may cause icemakers not to harvest or to have other ice production problems. If the freezer temperature is hovering right around the thermostat temperature setting, the icemaker's thermostat may open and close, causing slow or intermittent ice production. If the freezer temperature is not low enough, check the refrigerator's temperature settings.

High freezer temperatures may also mean that the *refrigerator* has cooling problems such as defrost or sealed system malfunctions. If adjusting the controls doesn't lower the freezer temperature, see Chapters 4 and 5.

8-4(b) POWER SUPPLY

Check that the icemaker is getting power. Unplug it from the freezer wall socket and see if you have power between at least two of the terminals.

8-4(c) WATER SUPPLY

Check also that the icemaker is getting water. If possible, unmount the icemaker from the freezer wall and manually initiate a harvest cycle. Collect and measure the water fill. (While you're at it, check it for bad smell or taste, too.) If no water comes out, check that the fill solenoid valve is getting voltage, and check for continuity through the solenoid as described in Chapter 1. A clogged or defective water valve or fill switch should be replaced.

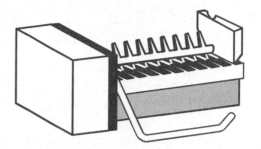

8-5 CRESCENT CUBE ICEMAKERS

These icemakers are used in many different brands. The design of the crescent-cube machine is, in my opinion, far superior to others. They crank out lots of ice pretty darned reliably. Conversion kits are available to change most refrigerators from other icemaker designs to the crescent cube design if desired.

NOTE: *These icemakers are virtually commodity items at this point in time. In many circumstances it may be cheaper and easier to buy a new one than to make a repair. Check your local prices.*

There are three types of these machines; a "compact" design, a "modular" design, and an electronic version. You can tell the difference between them when you remove the plastic cover. (Figure X-2) The "modular" design has a thick grey plastic plate to which the motor mounts. The "compact" design has a metal plate. The electronic one has a circuit board and an on-off rocker switch on the right side of the icemaker head.

Most of the symptoms and the malfunctions between the three designs are similar. However, the internal differences between them are pretty pronounced, so testing and troubleshooting are quite different.

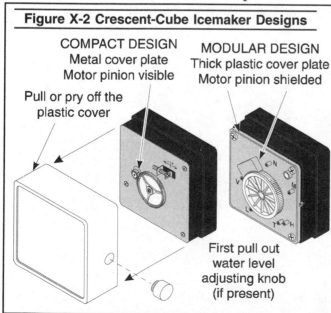

Figure X-2 Crescent-Cube Icemaker Designs

COMPACT DESIGN
Metal cover plate
Motor pinion visible

MODULAR DESIGN
Thick plastic cover plate
Motor pinion shielded

Pull or pry off the plastic cover

First pull out water level adjusting knob (if present)

8-5(a) MODULAR CRESCENT CUBE DESIGN

OPERATION

The harvest cycle on these icemakers is thermostatically triggered. A thermostat inside the icemaker head is pressed against the ice mold. (Figure X-3) When the mold gets down to about 17 degrees, the thermostat closes and starts the drive motor, and energizes the mold heater. Very shortly thereafter, a cam on the drive shaft closes the holding switch, keeping the motor circuit energized even after the thermostat opens back up. The shaft rotates clockwise until the ejection fingers press against the ice. The motor then stalls, with the ejection fingers applying pressure to the ice, until the mold heats up enough for the cubes to separate from the mold. The fingers then continue pushing the ice out of the mold. Sometime during the harvest cycle the thermostat opens and the mold heater shuts off, but the holding switch keeps the motor turning. Shortly after the fingers pass through the 12 o'clock position, another cam attached to the driveshaft closes the fill switch for about 7-8 seconds and the mold fills with water. Shortly thereafter, the holding switch opens, stopping the drive motor, and the icemaker is ready for another freeze cycle.

There is a third switch in the icemaker head; the shutoff switch. This switch is activated by the ice level sensor arm. If the ice level in the bin is too high, or if you raise the arm to the shutoff position, this switch opens and interrupts the thermostat circuit. The icemaker then will not enter a harvest cycle until the sensor arm is allowed to return to its full down position. During the harvest cycle, a cam raises the sen-

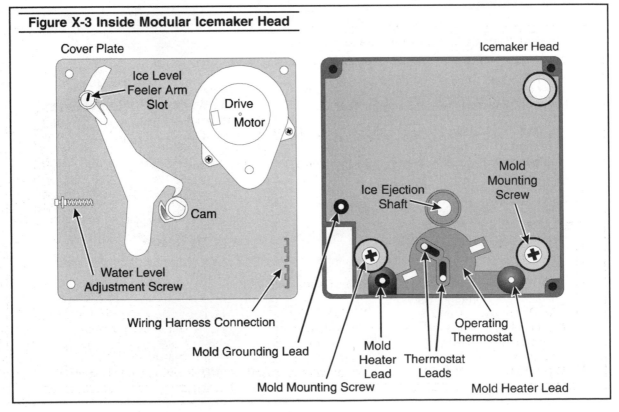

Figure X-3 Inside Modular Icemaker Head

Cover Plate

Ice Level Feeler Arm Slot

Drive Motor

Cam

Water Level Adjustment Screw

Wiring Harness Connection

Mold Grounding Lead

Icemaker Head

Mold Mounting Screw

Ice Ejection Shaft

Mold Heater Lead

Mold Mounting Screw

Thermostat Leads

Operating Thermostat

Mold Heater Lead

sor arm and opens the shut-off switch, but the holding switch keeps the motor turning. After the ice drops into the bin, the sensor arm drops back down into the fully-lowered position and closes the shut-off switch unless the ice level prevents it.

The water fill on these icemakers should be about 140 cc's and take 7.5 seconds. There is an adjustment screw on the right side of the icemaker head; one full turn equals 40cc's. Some models have water level adjustment dials on the right side of the plastic icemaker head cover that attach to this screw. This screw simply moves the fill switch closer to the cam on the drive shaft, keeping it open longer, or vice-versa. The maximum adjustment on these machines is one full turn in either direction; any more will damage the icemaker head. When adjusting the level, do it gently and do not attempt to force it AT ALL.

TROUBLESHOOTING

Aside from water supply problems, what usually goes wrong with these machines is that the thermostat (bimetal) fails. Typically, the symptom will be inoperation; it just won't be making any ice. If the mold is full of ice, jump the thermostat to see if the machine harvests normally. To jump the thermostat and trigger a harvest cycle, just jumper between the T and H test point holes. (Figure X-4) Leave the jumper in until you hear a "click," (this is the holding switch closing) then remove it. A defective thermostat can be replaced by removing the cover plate. When replacing the thermostat, put a dab of aluminum putty on the face of it (where it contacts the ice mold) to insure good contact and heat transfer from the ice mold.

Figure X-4 Modular Crescent Icemaker Test Points

With *NO POWER* to the icemaker, and ice election fingers in the "freeze" cycle position, test for resistance between these test points:

TO TEST:	Put Meter Leads in test points:	Meter Should Read
Motor	L and M	8800 Ohms
Mold Heater	L and H	72 Ohms

To bypass the thermostat and initiate a harvest cycle, jump between the "T" and "H" test points with a loop of wire

With *POWER ON THE ICEMAKER*, test for 110 Volts between these test points:

TO TEST:	Put Meter Leads in test points:	If Meter Reads Zero Volts:	If meter reads 110 Volts:
For Power	L and N	No power to icemaker	You have power to the icemaker
Mold Heater	L and H	Heater is off	Heater should be on
Motor	L and M	Motor is off	Motor should be on
Thermostat	T and H	Thermostat is closed	Thermostat is open
Water Valve	N and V	Water valve is closed	Water should be filling mold

MOLD HEATER FAILURE AND MOTOR FAILURE PROBLEMS

If the mold heater fails, the cubes will not separate from the mold and the icemaker harvest cycle would stall indefinitely. In this case, you would see the ejection fingers pressed against the ice, trying to eject it, but it would not eject. Under power, test for line voltage between the L and H test point holes; if it is energized, then power is going to the heater. Unplug and test for resistance between the same test points; the heater should test 72 ohms. If not, replace the mold.

If the drive motor isn't turning at a time when it should be, test for 110 volts between L and M to see if the motor is energized. Then unplug the icemaker and test resistance between the same test points. It should test at 8800 ohms. If not, replace the motor.

8-5(b) COMPACT CRESCENT CUBE DESIGN

OPERATION

These icemakers are very similar to the modular style icemakers in the previous section; the modular ones being a refinement of these machines. The water fill on these icemakers should be about 140 cc's and take 7.5 seconds. There is a water level adjustment screw inside the cover. Some have water level adjustment dials on the right side of the plastic icemaker head cover.

The harvest cycle on these icemakers is thermostatically triggered. A thermostat inside the icemaker head is pressed against the ice mold. (Figure X-5) (When replacing the thermostat, use a dab of aluminum putty to insure good contact and heat transfer from the ice mold.) When the mold gets

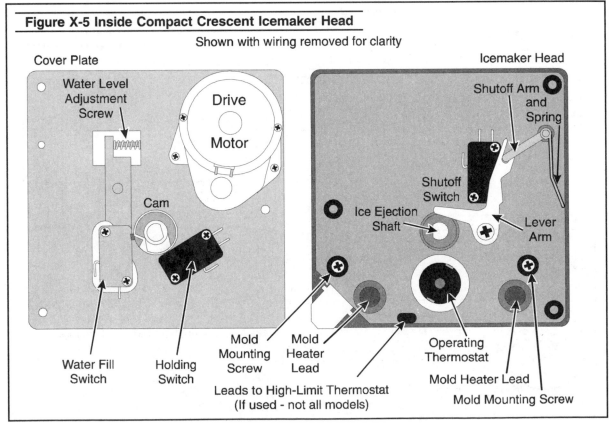

Figure X-5 Inside Compact Crescent Icemaker Head

Shown with wiring removed for clarity

Cover Plate

Icemaker Head

Water Level Adjustment Screw

Drive Motor

Shutoff Arm and Spring

Cam

Shutoff Switch

Ice Ejection Shaft

Lever Arm

Water Fill Switch

Holding Switch

Mold Mounting Screw

Mold Heater Lead

Operating Thermostat

Mold Heater Lead

Mold Mounting Screw

Leads to High-Limit Thermostat (If used - not all models)

down to about 17 degrees, the thermostat closes and starts the drive motor, and energizes the mold heater. Very shortly thereafter, a cam on the drive shaft closes the holding switch, keeping the motor circuit energized and turning even after the thermostat opens back up. The shaft rotates clockwise until the ejection fingers press against the ice. The motor then stalls, with the ejection fingers applying pressure to the ice, until the mold heats up enough for the cubes to separate from the mold. The fingers then continue pushing the ice out of the mold.

The thermostat stays closed throughout the first rotation of the ejection fingers. Near the completion of the first rotation, another cam attached to the driveshaft closes the fill switch, but

water fill does not occur. The shutoff switch is closed, and offers a lot less resistance than the water valve circuit. (Figure X-6) Electricity will follow the path of least resistance, so the water valve will not open unless the thermostat is open.

Sometime during the second rotation of the ejection fingers, the thermostat opens and the mold heater shuts off, but the holding switch keeps the motor turning. Near the completion of the second rotation, the fill switch closes again for about 7-8 seconds, and this time the mold fills with water. (Figure X-6) Shortly after the fill switch opens, and waterflow stops, the holding switch opens. This stops the drive motor, and the icemaker is ready for another freeze cycle.

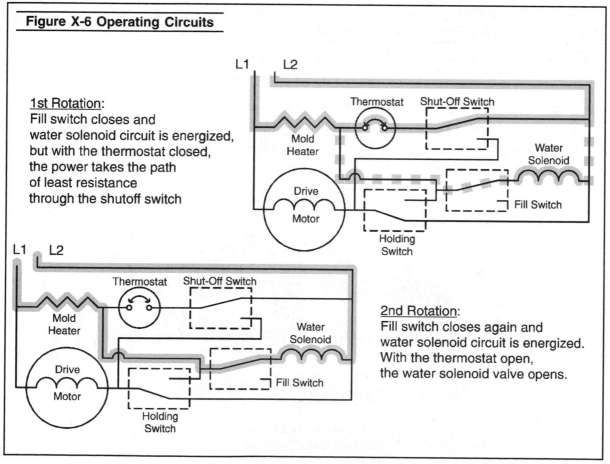

Figure X-6 Operating Circuits

1st Rotation:
Fill switch closes and water solenoid circuit is energized, but with the thermostat closed, the power takes the path of least resistance through the shutoff switch

2nd Rotation:
Fill switch closes again and water solenoid circuit is energized. With the thermostat open, the water solenoid valve opens.

There is a third switch in the icemaker head; the shutoff switch. This switch is activated by the ice level sensor arm. If the ice level in the bin is too high, or if you raise the arm to the shutoff position, this switch opens and interrupts the thermostat circuit. The icemaker then will not enter a harvest cycle until the sensor arm is allowed to return to its full down position. During the harvest cycle, a cam raises the sensor arm and opens the shut-off switch, but the holding switch is still closed, which keeps the motor turning. After the ice drops into the bin, the sensor arm drops back down into the fully-lowered position and closes the shut-off switch unless the ice level prevents it.

TROUBLESHOOTING

These machines are subject to most of the same malfunctions as their more modern modular cousins; namely, thermostat, mold heater and drive motor failures. However, they do not have test points, so they do not share the same testing procedures.

To initiate a harvest cycle, turn the motor pinion counterclockwise (Figure X-7) until the holding switch closes and the drive motor begins turning under its own power.

These machines also seem to have a problem with the motor pinion gear drive gear slipping off the drive motor shaft. When you remove the plastic cover, you will see the motor gear turning and disengaged from the larger ejection drive gear. The motor gear can be pressed back on and glued with superglue.

Some of these machines have a "chiclet"-type thermal fuse (figure X-8) attached to the underside of the ice mold, near the icemaker head. If this fuse blows, the icemaker will not harvest, nor will the motor start when you try to manually initiate a harvest cycle. These fuses are non-resettable; they must be replaced. To test, just remove power from the icemaker and check continuity through the fuse. If the fuse has blown, the ice mold has overheated at some time. Since the heater is in series with the thermostat, it usually means the thermostat is staying closed or that the motor has stalled for too long while trying to eject ice.

There are three micro switches inside the icemaker head. (Figure X-5) The shut-off switch is activated by the ice level sensor arm and prevents the harvest cycle from taking place unless the arm is down. The other two microswitches are the waterfill switch and the holding switch, both cam-operated. The thermostat initiates the harvest cycle, but the holding switch keeps the drive motor turning through the complete cycle, even after the thermostat has opened.

8-5(c) ELECTRONIC CRESCENT CUBE DESIGN

These machines cannot be serviced; they must be replaced when defective. Fortunately, they're pretty much commodity items at this point, and can be replaced for well under a hundred bucks.

Figure X-7 Initiating a Harvest Cycle

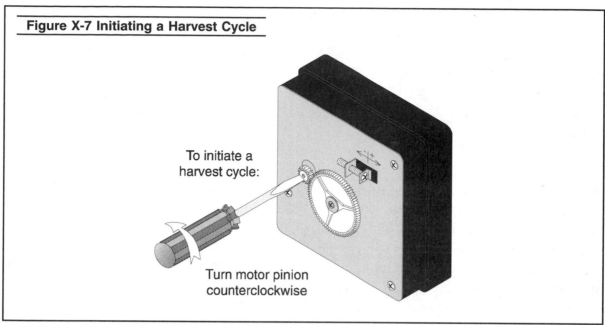

To initiate a
harvest cycle:

Turn motor pinion
counterclockwise

Figure X-8 "Chiclet-" Type Thermal Fuse

View: Underside of Icemaker

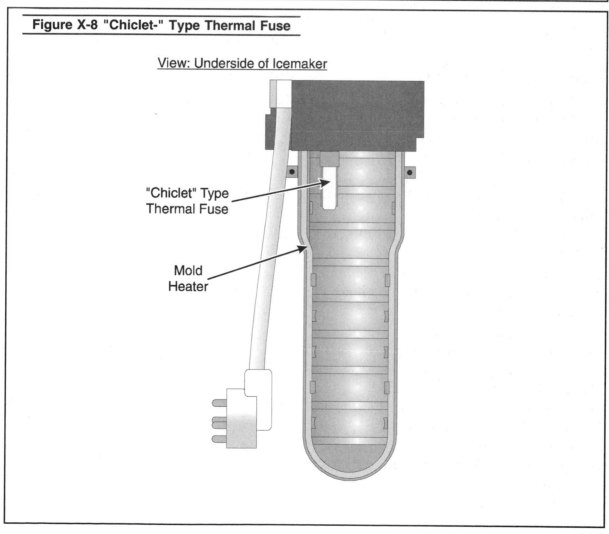

"Chiclet" Type
Thermal Fuse

Mold
Heater

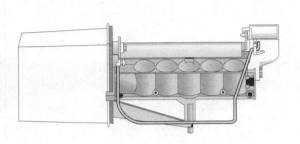

8-6 GE "BULLET" OR "BARREL" CUBE MACHINES

These machines produce five cylindrical cubes per harvest. The water fill should be 70 to 85 cc's, or about 6 seconds.

Parts *are* commonly available for these machines;. however, you may want to consider converting to the crescent-cube design. Crescent cube machines produce far more ice, far more reliably. And at the time of this writing, conversion kits are available for about 75-100 bucks. If there is an ice dispenser in the door, you may need to turn down the crescent cube size a little to get the cubes to go through the door properly.

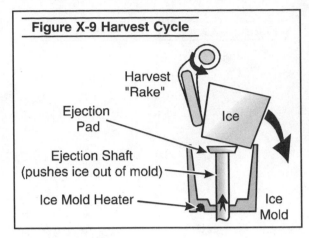

Figure X-9 Harvest Cycle

OPERATION

The harvest cycle begins thermostatically at about 16 degrees. A heater activates to release the cubes from the mold. An ejection shaft through the bottom of the ice mold is attached to an ejection pad, which pushes the cubes vertically from the mold. The cubes are then swept off the mold and into the bin by a "harvest rake." (Figure X-9)

On the start of ejection, the first switch of a three-leaf switch closes. (Figure X-10) This is the holding switch, and it keeps the motor turning even after the thermostat closes again. The second contact in the leaf switch is for the water fill. It is activated by the bump on the cam for about six seconds near the end of the cycle. There is a water level adjustment screw embedded into the cam.

There is another switch in the icemaker head; the shutoff switch. (Figure X-11) This switch is activated by the ice level sensor arm. If the ice level in the bin is

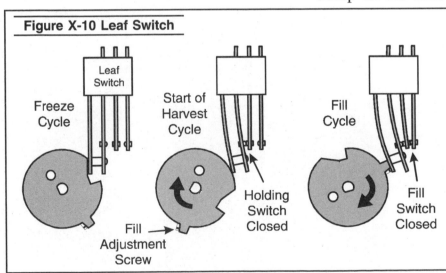

Figure X-10 Leaf Switch

too high, or if you raise the arm to the shutoff position, this switch opens and interrupts the thermostat circuit. The icemaker then will not enter a harvest cycle until the sensor arm is allowed to return to its full down position. During the harvest cycle, the mechanism raises the sensor arm and opens the shut-off switch, but the holding switch keeps the motor turning. After the harvest rake sweeps the ice into the bin, the sensor arm drops back down into the fully-lowered position and closes the shut-off switch, unless the ice level prevents it.

Some models also have a safety (hi-limit) thermostat, which prevents accidental overheating of the ice mold.

TROUBLESHOOTING

Almost invariably, service on these machines involve a leak around the ejection shaft and ice slabbing in the bin. There is a shaft seal replacement kit available; it's a tricky installation requiring a couple of special tools.

About the only other fairly common complaint is thermostat failure. The icemaker will not be producing ice, and you're sure the freezer is cold enough, but manually jumping the thermostat produces a harvest.

There are two test connections on the underside of the icemaker head. In both, a small rectangular plug in the bottom of the icemaker head can be removed to reveal two small holes. (Figure X-12) The black plug is for the safety (hi-limit) thermostat, which prevents accidental overheating of the ice mold; not all models have this thermostat or this plug. The white plug is for the operating thermostat. If the thermostat is bad, replace it.

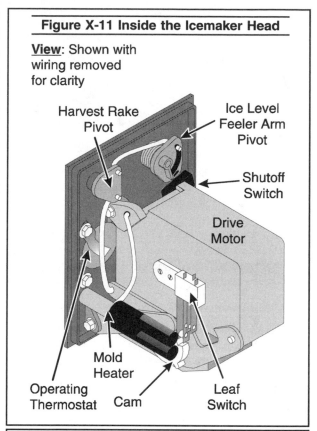

Figure X-11 Inside the Icemaker Head

View: Shown with wiring removed for clarity

Harvest Rake Pivot

Ice Level Feeler Arm Pivot

Shutoff Switch

Drive Motor

Mold Heater

Operating Thermostat

Cam

Leaf Switch

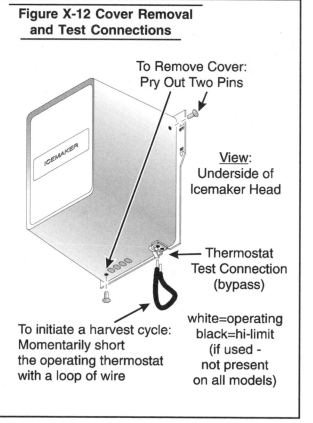

Figure X-12 Cover Removal and Test Connections

To Remove Cover: Pry Out Two Pins

ICEMAKER

View: Underside of Icemaker Head

Thermostat Test Connection (bypass)

white=operating black=hi-limit (if used - not present on all models)

To initiate a harvest cycle: Momentarily short the operating thermostat with a loop of wire

Icemaker Head Towards Rear of Freezer

8-7 ADMIRAL-TYPE FLEX-TRAY

The ice mold of these icemakers is in front of the head as you look into the freezer compartment. When the harvest cycle is initiated, it takes about eight minutes for the tray to rotate completely around and refill. The lower the freezer temperature, the more ice it will produce. Above 19 degrees, it will not produce ice at all.

You can tell if the motor is turning by looking at the end of the motor shaft as shown on the illustration. (Figure X-13)

You can initiate a harvest cycle manually by pushing the two switches as shown in the illustration; (Figure X-13) the lower left away from the shaft, and the right center towards the shaft, while simultaneously slowly and firmly turning the ice tray clockwise until the motor takes over and starts turning the tray. (It sorta takes three hands or strong thumbs to do this) Observe the whole cycle, especially the twisting action when the tray is inverted. As the tray fills, watch beneath the ice mold for any water leakage. The water fill should be about 180-220 cc's and take about 13-14 seconds. There is an adjustment screw on the right side of the head, but the factory glues it in place during construction. In fact, the factory doesn't want you messing with these machines at all; if they malfunction, the solution is to replace them. I have had a couple of these icemakers apart and I'd have to agree with the factory in this case. Just replace them. Trust me. After you replace your old one, try pulling it apart and reassembling it and you'll see what I mean.

A conversion kit is available to convert the refrigerator to a crescent-cube design, and I would highly recommend it. They are not difficult to install, although some installations require minor cabinet modifications and/or water level changes. Instructions will be included in the conversion kit.

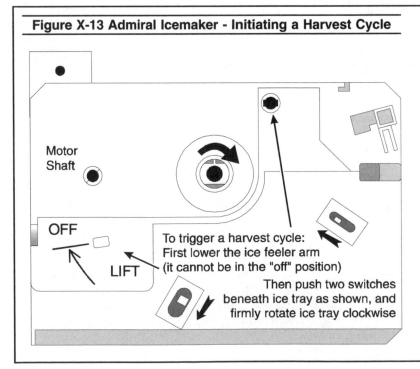

Figure X-13 Admiral Icemaker - Initiating a Harvest Cycle

Motor Shaft

OFF

LIFT

To trigger a harvest cycle:
First lower the ice feeler arm
(it cannot be in the "off" position)

Then push two switches
beneath ice tray as shown, and
firmly rotate ice tray clockwise

During the harvest cycle in this design, the twisting action of the ice tray ends with a relatively violent SNAP! Over time this can have several adverse effects.

The icemaker can begin to pull its wall mounts out of the freezer wall. If this happens, the icemaker will not be level. Cubes on the high side of the mold may be too small, while cubes on the low side may be too large or even slab together, and fail to eject.

The plastic mold (tray) can crack, especially around the hub. (Figure X-14) The tray may leak, or not twist, preventing proper cube ejection.

If the spacer (bushing) around the shaft (behind the icemaker head) is worn or missing, the tray will not be held close enough to the head for the tab on the tray to catch the tab on the head and twist properly. (Figure X-14) The ice will not eject properly, causing slabbing.

The plastic tray in these machines seems to be more prone to scale and calcium buildup than other designs, causing improper ejection and slabbing.

I'm not sure what causes it, but if you hear the icemaker ticking like a clock, and it's annoying you, replace the icemaker head.

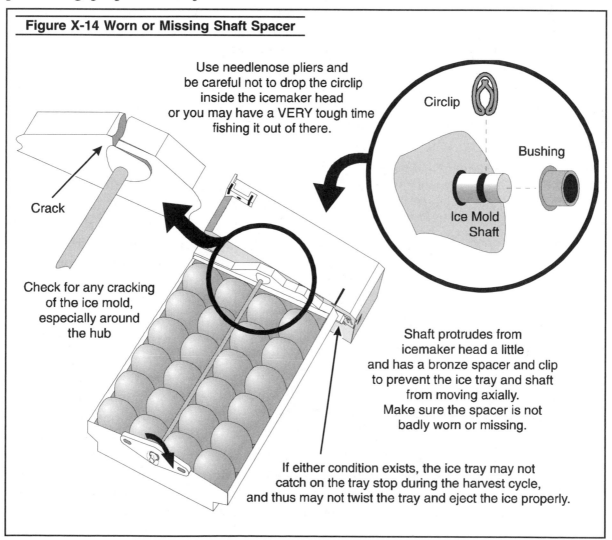

Figure X-14 Worn or Missing Shaft Spacer

Use needlenose pliers and be careful not to drop the circlip inside the icemaker head or you may have a VERY tough time fishing it out of there.

Circlip

Bushing

Ice Mold Shaft

Crack

Check for any cracking of the ice mold, especially around the hub

Shaft protrudes from icemaker head a little and has a bronze spacer and clip to prevent the ice tray and shaft from moving axially. Make sure the spacer is not badly worn or missing.

If either condition exists, the ice tray may not catch on the tray stop during the harvest cycle, and thus may not twist the tray and eject the ice properly.

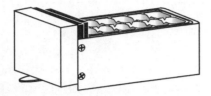

8-8 WHIRLPOOL/KENMORE FLEX-TRAY DESIGN

In Whirlpool flex-tray icemakers, first check that the icemaker drive motor is turning. It should turn constantly while the compressor is running. If it is, there are a number of things that could be causing the icemaker to stop making cubes, but the solution to all of them seems to be to throw a new gear and pin set in both the front and back of the icemaker head. (The ejection gears are in the fromt of the head; the defrost timing gears are under a cover on the backside of the head) This is true even

if the gears look allright to begin with, but especially if any teeth are stripped on the drive gear, or if the tray is stopped in a position other than upright. Gear alignment instructions are included with the new gears.

There is no way to manually initiate a harvest cycle in these machines. When you replace and realign the gears and reinstall the icemaker, it will immediately enter a harvest cycle and fill with water.

Time only accumulates on these icemakers when the cold control (the refrigerator's thermostat) is closed and the compressor is running. If the doors remain closed, the ambient air temperature (outside of the fridge) is low, and the compressor doesn't run much, you may experience low ice production. In this case, set the cold control as cold as it will go to increase run time. There is also a kit available, no. 482763 with a special drive motor and fill switch. To increase ice production, the kit decreases the cycle time to 1-1/2 hours instead of 2 hours.

Part of the refrigerator's defrost function is built into the icemaker in these machines. Thus, the icemaker must be plugged in at all times, even if it's not being used to make ice. If you no longer use the icemaker and wish to remove it from your machine, a module is available that replaces the icemaker with a smaller "box" unit that just performs the defrost function. Ask your appliance parts distributor for details.

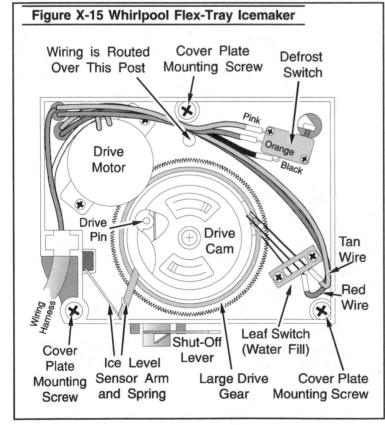

Figure X-15 Whirlpool Flex-Tray Icemaker

Wiring is Routed Over This Post
Cover Plate Mounting Screw
Defrost Switch
Pink
Orange
Black
Drive Motor
Drive Pin
Drive Cam
Tan Wire
Red Wire
Wiring Harness
Cover Plate Mounting Screw
Ice Level Sensor Arm and Spring
Shut-Off Lever
Large Drive Gear
Leaf Switch (Water Fill)
Cover Plate Mounting Screw

WHIRLPOOL / KENMORE
ADC Defrost / Diagnosis

Maximum defrost cycle time is 21 minutes.
First defrost is 6 hours after initial plugin (cumulative compressor runtime.)
Minimum time between defrost cycles is 8 hours.
Maximum time between defrost cycles is 100 hours.
The ADC adjusts the defrost interval according to compressor runtime, and length of the last defrost cycle.

ASSUMING that the fridge has been on and running,
and the terminating thermostat is closed,
defrost is initiated in most models by turning the cold control on and off as follows:

OFF for 15 seconds, then ON for 5 seconds, then
OFF for 15 seconds, then ON for 5 seconds, then
OFF for 15 seconds, then ON for 5 seconds, then turn the cold control off.

The defrost heater should start heating up within 8 seconds.
To terminate defrost, unplug the fridge.

Note that the ADC will only enter the defrost mode if the terminating thermostat is closed. You will hear a click as the relay on the ADC board switches from the "cool" mode to the "defrost" mode. If the terminating thermostat is open, you will hear a second click and the fridge will return to the cooling mode; you probably have a bad terminating thermostat.

If the defrost heater does not come on at all, try initiating defrost as follows:
Unplug the fridge for 30 seconds.
While it is unplugged, turn the cold control off.
Then plug the fridge back in.

The defrost heater should start heating up within 8 seconds.
The ADC board relay will also click as described above.

If the above procedure caused the heater to heat up, the ADC board is probably bad; replace it.

If the defrost heater does not heat up, test the defrost heater and terminating thermostat. You *can* test them for continuity together, without opening up the evaporator. Find the test plug in the wiring harness with a brown lead and a pink lead (inside the control box.) Unplug the fridge and disconnect the ADC, then test for continuity between this brown lead and any white lead. You are measuring resistance through the heater; you should see *some* resistance, and *some* continuity. If not, the heater is bad.

Now test between the brown and pink leads. You are now testing continuity through the terminating thermostat. If the evaporator has been running and the terminating thermostat is cold, you should see continuity. If not, the terminating thermostat is bad.

GENERAL ELECTRIC / HOTPOINT / RCA
including PROFILE, ETERNA and SELECT models
ADC Defrost / Diagnosis

These machines use a very complex "control board" accessible at the right rear of the refrigerator. In addition to defrost functions, this board gets inputs from *thermistors* and controls the operation of fans, damper doors and heaters throughout the refrigerator, as well as water-in-door, icemaker, ice crusher and auger functions.

Thermistors are simply variable resistors. The resistance of a thermistor varies inversely with the temperature of the thermistor; the lower the temperature, the higher the resistance. Thus a thermistor can measure the temperature in a space and translate that into an electrical signal that a logic board can use.

For example, if the temperature in a space gets too low, the thermistor will tell the logic board, and the logic board can close an air damper to warm the space a little.

Defrost intervals (time between defrost cycles) are controlled by the frequency and duration of freezer and fresh food door openings, defrost heater runtime and compressor runtime.

Maximum defrost cycle time is 45 minutes.
Minimum time between defrost cycles is 8 hours. (accumulated compressor runtime)
Maximum time between defrost cycles is 60 hours. (accumulated compressor runtime)

If the refrigerator is not defrosting, because of the complexity of the control system, there could be a number of reasons.

Test the defrost heater and terminating thermostat as follows: unplug the fridge, and unplug the blue connector from the control board. Using an ammeter, test the resistance between the blue wire on the blue connector, and the orange wire (pin 9, the last pin) on the J7 connector (this connector is marked N on the board, for "Neutral.") You should see 22 Ohms of resistance. You are testing through the defrost heater and terminating thermostat, so if you get either an open reading or no resistance, one of these components is bad. When you reinstall the blue connector and turn the power back on, the defrost heater should heat up. If not, the terminating thermostat is bad.

There are two thermistors in the evaporator compartment, near the top of the evap. They are a control thermistor and a high-temp thermistor, which basically does the same thing as the terminating thermostat. You can test these thermistors according to the table to the right. However, it is easier to just replace one or both of them. (They are both the same thermistor.)

If the heater, thermostat and thermistors test out OK, replace the main board.

Thermistor Values		
Temp F	Temp C	ohms
-40	-40	166.8
-31	-35	120.5
-22	-30	88
-13	-25	65
-4	-20	48.4
5	-15	36.4
14	-10	27.6
23	-5	21
32	0	16.3
41	5	12.7
50	10	10
59	15	7.8
68	20	6.2
77	25	5
86	30	4
95	35	3.2

FRIGIDAIRE MODELS, including
GIBSON, TAPPAN, KELVINATOR, and WHITE-WESTINGHOUSE
ADC Defrost / Diagnosis

On the initial plugin, or when power is restored to the fridge after a power outage:

If terminating thermostat is open, the fridge enters a compressor (cooling) cycle.
If the terminating thermostat is closed, the first defrost cycle occurs 1 hour
after initial plug-in.

Maximum defrost cycle time is 24 minutes.
Minimum time between defrost cycles is 6 hours. (compressor runtime)
Maximum normal clock time between defrost cycles is 12 hours.
Maximum time between defrost cycles (in "vacation" mode) is 72 hours.
Vacation mode is not entered unless the door has not been opened in *at least* 24 hours.

Note that the ADC will only enter the defrost mode if the terminating thermostat is closed. If the terminating thermostat is open when defrost is initiated, the ADC board will wait for six minutes and then return to the cooling mode.

ASSUMING that the fridge has been on and running,
and the terminating thermostat is closed,
defrost is initiated by pressing the door (light) switch
at least five times within six seconds.
The defrost heater should start heating up within 8 seconds.

If the above procedure caused the heater to heat up, the ADC board is probably bad; replace it.

If the defrost heater does not heat up, test the defrost heater, terminating thermostat and cold control for continuity as follows:

Unplug the fridge from the wall. Unplug the ADC board from its connector.
Test the connector for continuity between the following leads:
Defrost Heater = DEF TERM (blue) to DEF OUT (brown).
Terminating Thermostat = DEF TERM (blue) to NEUTRAL (lt blue).
Cold Control = COLD CONTROL (orange) to L1 (black).

Replace the defective component.

**MAYTAG, JENN-AIR, ADMIRAL, MAGIC CHEF
ADC Defrost / Diagnosis**

Maximum defrost cycle time is approximately 23 minutes.

The ADC adjusts the next defrost interval (time until the next defrost cycle) based on how long the defrost heater was energized during the last defrost cycle. The length of the defrost cycle is determined by the terminating thermostat. Logically, then, the shorter the defrost cycle, the less frost needed to be melted, so the longer the compressor can be run until the next defrost cycle.

To intitate defrost, find the ADC board. In Maytag-built machines, it is inside the temperature control housing, which also contains the food compartment (cold control) and freezer controls.

The ADC board should have six terminals: DEF HTR, COMP, L2, DEF TSTAT, TEST and L1.

Make sure the compressor is running. If you try to initiate defrost without the compressor running, it will cycle through the test mode in two seconds, andthere will not be any current draw through the defrost heater.

Use a jumper wire to short between L1 and test for a few seconds. This will place the unit into a 23-minute defrost mode. The defrost heater will heat up. If you have an ammeter, the heater will be drawing about 4 to 5 amps.

If the above procedure caused the heater to heat up, the ADC board is probably bad; replace it.

If the defrost heater does not energize, test the defrost heater and terminating thermo-stat as described in section 4-5(f).

Index

V

Volt-Ohm Meter 3.4
   How to Use 3.5, 3.6
Voltage
   Testing 3.5
VOM. *See* Volt-Ohm Meter

W

Warbling Noise. *See* Noises
Water 7.4
   On Floor 6.1
Whistling Noise. *See* Noises

Also Available from EB Marketing Group
Brand-Specific Dryer & Top-Loading Washer Manuals!
for those who want a little LESS...
Our brand-specific manuals have the same high quality instructions and illustrations
as our all-brand manuals, at a new low price!

7th Edition
Whirlpool Dryer Repair
ISBN 1-890386-36-7   Part No. EBWD

7th Edition
Whirlpool Washer Repair
ISBN 1-890386-35-9   Part No. EBWW

Whirlpool-brand manuals include
Kenmore, Kitchenaid, Estate
and Roper Brand Machines

7th Edition
GE/Hotpoint Dryer Repair
ISBN 1-890386-38-3   Part No. EBGD

7th Edition
GE/Hotpoint Washer Repair
ISBN 1-890386-37-5   Part No. EBGW

GE-brand manuals include
Hotpoint, late-model RCA, and
JC Penney (Penncrest) Brand Machines

7th Edition
Maytag Dryer Repair
ISBN 1-890386-40-5   Part No. EBMD

7th Edition
Maytag Washer Repair
ISBN 1-890386-39-1   Part No. EBMW

Available from EB Marketing Group